INVENTION,
DISCOVERY,
AND
CREATIVITY

A. D. MOORE, in a long and active life, has been an electrical engineer, teacher, inventor, public servant, lecturer, and author. He earned his degree in Electrical Engineering in 1915 from Carnegie Institute of Technology. The following year he joined the teaching staff of the University of Michigan and began a teaching career there that was to last for more than forty-seven years. During his tenure, Professor Moore received his M.S.E. from that university (in 1923), and at his retirement he became professor emeritus. A secondary career as a lawmaker started in 1940 when he was elected to serve on the City Council of Ann Arbor, Michigan, the beginning of seventeen years of service on the Council.

"A.D.," as most people call him, writes short stories and poems, plays three-cushion billiards like an expert, and has traveled thousands of "station wagon miles" since retirement five years ago, lecturing to high school science clubs, college students, and professional engineers, and demonstrating his electrostatic generators and fluid mappers—his own term for the simulation of fields by fluid flow. He still maintains his office-laboratory on the Michigan campus, where he recently discovered and developed a new line of phenomena in the field of electrospherics and magnetospherics.

Professor Moore has contributed numerous articles to the scientific journals, and is the author of *Electrostatics* in the Science Study Series. He has been an active member of Tau Beta Pi for over fifty years, and a member of Sigma Xi, Eta Kappa Nu, and Phi Kappa Phi. He has been Head Mentor at the University of Michigan; president of the University Club, the Quadrangle Club, and the Science Research Club; he is a Fellow and Life Member of the Institute of Electrical and Electronics Engineers, and a member of the Speaker Bureau of the Detroit Edison Company. Professor Moore estimates that he has played a part in the education of "literally thousands" of students and young engineers, a fact that gives him special qualifications to write about scientific creativity.

A. D. MOORE

INVENTION,
DISCOVERY,
AND
CREATIVITY

Doubleday & Company, Inc.
Garden City, New York

To Jo
for her constant faith
and encouragement in
this project

Library of Congress Catalog Card Number 69–10970
Copyright © 1969 by Doubleday & Company, Inc.
All Rights Reserved
Printed in the United States of America

ACKNOWLEDGMENTS:

PLACES AND PEOPLE

As to places, this book was born, not in one author's paradise, but three: my laboratory; our Canadian retreat; and the basement of a daughter's South Dakota home. To each, my thanks, for its own special quality and inspirational value. And I am especially indebted to former Chairman of Electrical Engineering Hansford W. Farris and to present Chairman Joseph E. Rowe, for enabling me to retain, as a retiree, the laboratory in which I work and demonstrate, and which serves as the indispensable base for my lecture trips.

As to people, I am indebted to many. Lewis E. Walkup, Gordon K. Teal, and James M. Lafferty have kindly contributed to Chapter Eight. Comments I appreciate have come from Dr. Wilson P. Tanner, psychologist, and Dr. Peter A. Franken, physicist, who read appropriate parts of the manuscript.

Here at the College of Engineering, University of Michigan, those who have read the whole manuscript and so helpfully commented on it are Dean Gordon Van Wylen; Associate Dean H. W. Farris, Mrs. Farris, and son Lawrence; Assistant to Dean Raymond E. Carroll; faculty members Donald T. Greenwood of Aerospace; Elmer G. Gilbert, Information and Control; Jerome H. Hemmye, Mechanical; and Edward E. Hucke, Metallurgical.

Elsewhere, my thanks for reading the manuscript go out to James M. Lafferty of General Electric, and son Roland; Dr. Jo C. Moore, daughter; Dr. John D. Goodman; Mrs. Goodman, our daughter, and granddaughter Lee; Del Coates; Dean A. K. Steigerwalt, Business Administration, The Detroit Institute of Technology; and Dean Myron Tribus, Engineering, Dartmouth College. Ralph M. Swingle, Assistant General Patent Counsel, Westinghouse Electric Corporation, kindly took the time to furnish me with much of the history of the Spencer disc story in Chapter Thirteen; and E. F. Kurtz, Manager, Division Patents at Metals & Controls, gave further assistance in filling it in.

I am especially grateful to my wife, for her high interest in this project and for reading back to me the several versions; and to the Series editor, Andrea Balchan, whose encouragement, incisive comments, and suggestions helped so much to make this a better book than it would otherwise have been.

My appreciation goes out to all those who have encouraged me to proceed in this venture, and to those who thoughtfully gave or sent references and actual items, some of which were simply invaluable to me. Space will not permit listing the more than one hundred items, papers, and books from which ideas and material were drawn. However, a selected list does appear at the end, as Recommended Reading.

CONTENTS

Acknowledgments: Places and People / v

The Science Study Series / xi

Introduction / xii

The Science Study Series offers to students and to the general public the writing of distinguished authors on the most stirring and fundamental topics of science, from the smallest known particles to the whole universe. Some of the books tell of the role of science in the world of man, his technology and civilization. Others are biographical in nature, telling the fascinating stories of the great discoverers and their discoveries. All the authors have been selected both for expertness in the fields they discuss and for ability to communicate their special knowledge and their own views in an interesting way. The primary purpose of these books is to provide a survey within the grasp of the young student or the layman. Many of the books, it is hoped, will encourage the reader to make his own investigations of natural phenomena.

The Series, which now offers topics in all the sciences and their applications, had its beginning in a project to revise the secondary schools' physics curriculum. At the Massachusetts Institute of Technology during 1956 a group of physicists, high school teachers, journalists, apparatus designers, film producers, and other specialists organized the Physical Science Study Committee, now operating as part of Educational Development Center, Newton, Massachusetts. They pooled their knowledge and experience toward the design and creation of aids to the learning of physics. Initially their effort was supported by the National Science Foundation, which has continued to aid the program. The Ford Foundation, the Fund for the Advancement of Education, and the Alfred P. Sloan Foundation have also given support. The Committee has created a textbook, an extensive film series, a laboratory guide, especially designed apparatus, and a teachers' source book.

Introductions are not easy to write. Not for me, and I suspect others have the same trouble. In the midst of my fidgeting and stalling, an idea came to mind. Looking around my laboratory, I found five things. Two were plaster cylinders, an inch wide and an inch high. One was a plaster cylinder two inches wide and two inches high. And two were shiny aluminum rods, a couple of inches long. I laid these on a bare table. On a sheet of paper, I typed these words:

CAN YOU USE THESE OBJECTS IN SUCH

A WAY AS TO MAKE THEM INTO A MODEL.

OF SOMETHING YOU ARE NOW TEACHING,

OR HAVE TAUGHT?

Then, one by one, I brought in twelve of my younger colleagues. The subject was told to read the question, then do whatever he liked, and take all the time he wanted. My subjects all made the same guess you probably have already made: that I wanted to see what models they would make, and perhaps, how fast they would do it. Not at all. In Chapter Eight I tell what I was really after, and its possible bearing on creativity.

Creativity: interest in it has greatly expanded in recent years. Psychologists and others have made studies of it, and presented papers. Scientists and engineers are busily telling each other about it in speeches and in print. But you, the *future* scientist or engineer, still in school, have been "the forgotten man." We have studied you to some extent, but we have not been writing for you. This book is meant to fill that gap. This is *your* book.

After all, in a decade or so, who will be our younger creative contributors in art, music, medicine, business, industry, science?—and where are they now? They will be *you:* you who are now in high school, or should be. You, with your classmates (plus, let us add, some dropouts!) will be where we must count on *your* creativity in a real way. It will come surprisingly soon. Perhaps the most pressing thing we should be doing is to make sure you are persuaded that you *are* creative; that it is never too early to practice the art; and that factors are at work that can kill off your creativity if you don't watch out.

Having a high creative talent is no guarantee that you will know how to manage it to get the best results. There is some "know-how" to be learned, and I will do my utmost to present it herein. Another thing: I gravely doubt if creativity is something that can be allowed to rest in peace until suddenly, you need to yank it out and put it to use. It needs *practice.*

Those are some reasons for writing this book. But why, in particular, am *I* writing it? If you want to know the truth, the book insists on being written. I have had a long and deep interest in creativity. While teaching electrical engineering for about half a century, I have often lectured on invention, inventing, and patents. But more, there has been a lifetime of creative experience. I have been through the mill, time and again. I know what it is to try to discover or invent something; to try, and fail; and try again, perhaps many times—and then at last, getting the intense satisfaction of having it come through. There have been quite a few inventions made in one area or another. No, I do not mean that all this resulted in many patents. I am a teacher, not a businessman. I have taken out but one patent, and it was ahead of its time (and there's no money made *that* way!)

One of my deep interests has been to develop new devices as teaching aids, and new analogs for solving problems. My fluid mappers have seen use in teaching, and they solve some tough engineering problems. My electrostatic generators and other devices are teaching aids, and they are serving to awaken interest in a much-neglected field.

Prior to my retirement at the end of 1963, I had given many lecture-demonstrations around the country with those items, to colleges and universities, industrial firms, government and private research groups, national conventions, and the like. Since retiring, our station wagon has carried the equipment on lecture-demonstration tours for 38,000 miles throughout the United States and into Canada. This has brought me in touch with hundreds of faculty members, thousands of students, and thousands of engineers and scientists. As a member of the Speakers Bureau of The Detroit Edison Company, I have the privilege of giving electrostatics demonstrations to Science Clubs in high schools. When the youngsters flock around the generators to get shocked and have fun, I get a chance to see how their "minds tick." All this, plus giving lectures on creativity, has helped to stimulate the urge to write this book.

It is written for the creative person who will not be completely happy unless his creative urge is released and used. If, in giving it an outlet, you are not only happier, but you also add to your reputation, or income, or both, so much the better.

ONE

Are You Creative?

Of course you are. Boy or girl, man or woman: You have these words before you, and are reading them. This qualifies you as a human being. And that qualifies you to join the Creativity Club.

As you know, not one of the lower animals can read, and not one ever will. Perhaps some of them do what we call thinking, in an extremely limited way. But their lives and activities, rich and varied as they sometimes are, are nevertheless governed and limited by instincts and largely automatic responses. We humans have a brain with which we think. We have a capacity for reliving the past. We are able to anticipate the future. If an animal meets a difficulty, it may merely turn aside, and always thereafter do the same. To us, a difficulty is a challenge. How can we surmount it? How can we change it? How might we even modify it and turn it into an advantage?

If a lower animal discovers something to its benefit, it wants more of the same. During a salmon run in an Alaskan river, a bear will return day after day to gorge on fish. When the run is ended, the bear goes back to a harder way to make a living. The bear can have no idea of doing anything about salmon, to improve his situation.

But man is a different animal. Like the bear, he cannot make the salmon run last longer. But being creative, he *can* think of making salmon come to streams and lakes where they did not come before. He plants salmon eggs in a lake where there are no salmon. The young are hatched, they go downstream to the sea to grow up, and then return to *that* lake. The salmon has that wonderful way of finding how to go back "home," and, pressured by instinct, it does it. And here is creative man, taking advantage of that remarkable ability and that blind instinct of the salmon, to add to his fishing sport and his food supply.

CREATIVITY IN THE VERY YOUNG

Can a child of twenty-two months display creativity? She can, and did. This was little Lee, a grandchild. On a visit to California, I took Lee for a walk, in Redlands. We ambled slowly around. We found a chicken yard, and solemnly observed the hens and the roosters. We wandered into an orange grove. Oranges on the trees. Oranges on the ground—lots of them. We wandered along. And Lee stopped, before four especially nice oranges. I could feel an idea developing: Take them home! Lee stooped and picked up one in each hand. That left two. Perhaps instinct told her to tuck the one in the right hand into the crook of the left elbow. She picked up the third orange. That left one. She again put the right-hand one into that same elbow crook. Whereupon, the one already there dropped out. Well then, try it again. Same thing happened. That little elbow basket would hold only one orange. A pause. And then this tiny child, whose vocabulary amounted to "eat," "light," and "water," and little else, went creative. She handed up two oranges to me, she picked up the other two, and we marched away in triumph. No doubt, she wondered why I exploded, and laughed until I was weak.

It is often noted that children are our most creative people. I believe it. And one of our most pressing problems is to find how to keep them that way, on up to adolescence and into maturity.

COMFORT AND CREATIVITY

Comfortable, conservative, complacent people do not create. Why should they? *They like it the way things are.* Creativity means *change* of some sort, and that means two kinds of disturbance. First, one's routines are disturbed *in order* to create. Second, if something new is created, it means change for the individual himself; and often, for others who are affected.

The creative process is not a comfortable thing. It involves urge, pressure. Some pressure is a part of the game, for the experience is both disturbing in some degree, and also tantalizing. I suspect that the feeling of *undue* pressure may be highest when one tries to be creative in an area for which there is too little inborn talent. I love good music, and have a strong and unfulfilled yearning to create some. I have managed to turn out two or three totally unimportant little songs for family and friends; and with much drudgery, have written the very simple musical scores for them. This was enough to expose a severe limitation: My facility for writing down music is extremely low. Thus, when I happen to think of trying to turn out a new tune, the worry about ever writing it down induces more pressure than I like. That is inhibiting. I give up, and turn to other things for which I am better fitted. This goes for all of us. We are all different, with our individual stronger and weaker capacities or talents. Striving to develop talents that aren't there has wrecked many a life. A prime factor in achieving happiness is in finding what we are pretty good at, and using these talents for living, and creativity.

A creative person will not be truly happy unless he does, from time to time, engage in creativity. He needs that outlet: to turn himself loose and do something about it. When he does, the urge brings on some pressure. This departure from comfort is just what he needs to get ahead with the idea that is riding him.

WRITING UNDER PRESSURE

Writing a book is a creative act; or perhaps better, a whole series of creative acts. What is your idea of how to write a book? Maybe it goes like this: Adopt a subject; make an outline; find some quiet place where there are no distractions, no interruptions, no pressures, and then, proceed! Would that it were that simple! Writers differ greatly among themselves as to how they manage the mechanics, the environment, and so on. Perhaps they differ as to pressure. With me, writing original material is a creative act that *inherently* involves pressure. These lines are being typed under what might be called creative pressure. That doesn't mean it is an unpleasant chore, or anything of the sort. Along with mild pressure is the tantalizing thought that others (even you!) may some day read the product.

Creativity can enter into every kind of human activity, and that of course includes writing. The highest writing pressure I ever feel comes in writing poetry. Picture me as I really am when trying that: getting an idea that demands expression; making a trial start; writing a line or two; wiggling around; writing; rubbing my eyes; erasing a word; going for a drink; scratching the back of my head; striving for a word that rhymes but also makes sense; failing; starting all over again on a new tack. . . . I ask you, is this the picture of a *relaxed* individual?

Technical writing, of which I have done plenty, is very different from that in two ways: The creative technical work has already been done; and the paper is in prose, far easier to manage than poetry. But writing a technical paper has its own creative requirements. It must be acceptable to fellow professionals. What about deciding on content, and order? There is the pressure to say it clearly; shall we *say* a certain thing, or shall we stop to draw a chart to replace a lot of words? These and other requirements put on the pressure to be creative—to write a paper that others will read, and read with appreciation.

SOME QUESTIONS ABOUT CREATIVITY

Do creative children become creative adolescents, and do creative adolescents become creative adults? Is the "brightest" youngster in your class also the most creative? That is, is there a close link, or correlation, between what what we call intelligence, and creativity? Or is there not? Do teachers tend to favor the pupils with the highest I.Q.? And what is their attitude toward the high-creative pupil?

Can creativity in a youngster be stifled, or will it survive anyway? Can moderate creativity be so effectively encouraged that it turns into high creativity? Is the capacity to be creative in a certain line inborn, or can it be acquired?

On an average basis, will equally creative men, given equal opportunity, be equally creative, or may it depend greatly on having good work habits?

If scientists or engineers are gathered in a research laboratory, will it be more important to provide them with every physical facility needed, or more important to make sure that the attitudes around the place are in good shape?

Will a highly creative person "just naturally" work out for himself, the best ways to use his abilities and thus make contributions, or is it that he could greatly benefit by knowing what has been learned about how to play the game?

Are men and women equally creative in all areas? (We will put off that delicate question until Chapter Thirteen).

It is much easier to ask questions than to get them answered. The creative process is concerned with the workings of the mind. And since we do have a mind, why not use it to find how the mind works? Why not just sit in that armchair, and concentrate, and make the mind's operations reveal its secrets? With exceptions, this is found to be a remarkably fruitless occupation. It just isn't that simple.

Until rather recently, these questions, and others that can be asked, have collected mostly opinions rather than good, solid answers. We still have far to go, but in the last two or three decades we have learned a good deal about this elusive activity called creativity. Various facets of the general problem are being studied by experts, from various angles or viewpoints. A book that would comprehensively review all that is already written, and include not only the pertinent studies but also the speculations that may yield further insight, would be interminably long. I have not the slightest desire to write such a book, and you would never read it anyway.

This is a short and simple book. Items listed in Recommended Reading at the back of the book will amplify on what I can cover here, and introduce you to areas not covered. As your interest in creativity grows, you will enjoy the constant and growing stream of new papers and books devoted to new interpretations and new researches in this fascinating and endless subject.

TWO

Ingenuity

> *Ingenuity:* quality or power of ready inven-
> tion; skill or cleverness in devising or com-
> bining; cleverness or aptness of design or
> contrivance. (Webster's International Dic-
> tionary, Second Edition, Unabridged)

It is no accident that *ingenuity, ingenious,* and *engineer*
sound so much alike. An engineer is supposed to be an
ingenious man, skilled in devising or combining. And if he
can go beyond just using his training to *design* engineering
products and is *creative,* he also has the "quality or power
of ready invention." His name, engineer, has gone through
many forms. One of these forms, *Ingenor,* was recently
adopted as the name of a semi-annual publication issued by
my own College of Engineering.

Of course, ingenuity first shows up in childhood. Children are highly creative. They are very busy little people,
forever trying things. A lot of this everlasting activity is
called "getting into mischief" by older people (and some of
it is!). But a great deal of this "trying things" is vitally
concerned with learning what this world is all about. The
child learns at a tremendous rate. The little child sees how
high he can stack up some blocks before they fall over.
Later on, he might try that with drinking glasses, but only
once.

Sometimes, the measure of a child's ingenuity is how
fast he has to run, to escape the consequences; or at least,

until the victims cool down a bit. Perhaps you can recall a time or two?

GETTING EVEN

"I'll get even with you!" When you were little, did you ever say that? Unless you were raised in a vacuum, you probably did. Little children are as lovable as can be. Sometimes. And as devilish as can be, sometimes. Which brings me to when I was a very small boy, smoldering under the urge to "get even." My older brother was an expert at teasing me, and I was sadly handicapped to think of ways to get even.

My ingenuity bestirred itself one summer day, and I had a brilliant idea. My precious companion at the time was half of a bicycle inner tube. On our farm, there was corn. I shelled enough corn from the cob to pretty well fill the tube. I plugged one end with the corn cob. Holding both ends up, I filled the tube with water. I sat down on our back porch, biding my time.

Then here came this older brother. I challenged him. Told him he couldn't blow that corn cob out. Scornfully, he seized the tube, took a deep breath, put his lips to the open end, and blew. Out went the cob. Also, water and shelled corn splattered all over the back porch. Of course, I counted on his having to clean up the mess. But just then, Mother came out of the back door, sized up the situation, and said, "Arthur, you clean that all up!"

I still think that was a marvelous experiment, showing "cleverness or aptness of design or contrivance." It just happened to backfire. Failed to meet with public acceptance. After which I had still more to smolder about. No: I never did catch up on my older brother.

PRACTICAL JOKES

When a situation is rigged with careful planning so that someone is fooled, we call it a practical joke. How that name ever got adopted is beyond me. You will notice that we have no name for its possible counterpart, the theoretical joke. Anyway, some practical jokes are so good, they are famous. I recall reading of a renowned character who took a room in a New York hotel. After he checked out, they found he had spent all of his time there making Jell-O. The bathtub was level full of Jell-O!

Dipping again into my boyhood, when I began to revel in the wonders of photography, I had *fixer,* which we called "hypo." Then, somewhere, I read of an interesting fact. After testing it out to make sure, I gave it a trial run on Mother. First, I spilled some iodine on a good linen tablecloth. What a stain! After calling her to see what had happened, I poured on some hypo, and the cloth was again white. I do not recall that she enjoyed the experiment.

Is it creative to give a word a new twist? Of course it is. A lot of our finest humor is made by hoisting a good old conservative word out of its favorite habitat, giving it an unexpected slant, and sending it on its way around the country to bring smiles to millions. Perhaps the pun is the most standardized example of word-twisting. Of course, we are plagued by far too many worthless puns, which may explain why many hold the pun to be the lowest form of humor. But a first-rate pun can be a gem of purest ray serene. Years ago, I heard one that must be one of the most elaborate ever invented. First, a question: "Why is a moth, flying around a candle, like a gate?" Then the answer (and if you don't get it, just repeat it out loud a few times): "If it keeps on it singes its wings."

Creativity often consists of finding a new use for something; or making a new combination of old elements. Thus, when we produce some humor by giving an old word a new twist, we are certainly being creative.

So: instead of humor being out of place in a serious discussion of creativity, it is very much in place. After a while, you will be reading about how our more creative young people have a high regard for a sense of humor, and how so many creative men have a sense of humor.

It just might be that some day, we may find that on the average, and with exceptions (notice how carefully I am leading up to this) the possession of a good sense of humor is the most reliable attribute of those who are most creative. It would not in the least surprise me.

SOME OLDER EXAMPLES OF INGENUITY

To live through the Arctic winter, the Eskimo must have seal meat, seal blubber, sealskin, and sinews with which to sew the sealskin clothing. Here and there, the seals keep breathing holes open in the ice sheet. They can stay down for extremely long periods, but must sooner or later come up to breathe. When a seal appears, the Eskimo is there with his spear. There is a difficulty, however. The seal has a very keen sense of hearing. When a hunter walks to a hole, no matter how quietly, the seals hear him, and avoid that hole. This could mean starvation for the Eskimo and his family. Question: Are you ingenious enough to solve this life-or-death problem, before I tell you further on about how the Eskimo solves it?

Now comes Otto von Guericke, one of the most able men of the seventeenth century. He took part in the Thirty Years' War, and served as the burgomaster of Magdeburg for thirty-five years. Along about 1645, he invented the first vacuum pump. Then, around 1660, he gave the world our first electrical machine. This, a friction-type electrostatic generator, was a smooth sulphur ball on a shaft. When the ball was turned and the hand was rubbed against it, "frictional electricity" was developed. Now, if you had been his young son, and he said to you, "I need a nice, smooth sphere of sulphur: Can you think of a way for me to have it made?" Could you? Von Guericke thought of a way. This ingenious man had a hollow glass sphere blown; he cast the molten sulphur in the glass shell. Then he cracked off the glass. Simple enough! Perhaps you think he just passed the hard problem on to the glassblower. Not at all. He *knew* the skillful things those fellows can do. Just as I know something about that, for I used to haunt the glass plant in my town when I was a kid. (I am a bit proud of the fact that a great-uncle of mine, a glassblower, blew the glass for the upper windows of the Capitol building in Washington, D.C.). No, it is no trick for a glassblower to produce a quite good hollow sphere.

Next, consider a highly successful portrait painter who gave up painting, turned to invention, and met hard times before his hopes were realized. This man's boyhood shows again that creative children are prone to get into mischief. I do hope that you will sometime read all about this man in *America's Greatest Inventors.*[*] We read there that as a little boy, ". . . he was playful, and not always easily disciplined." He went to Phillips Academy. "He was a healthy, vigorous boy, and delved into many books not required in his courses. Biographies of famous men appealed to him. . . ." Vigorous, playful, mischievous, *and* a broad reader! He became one of the most famous painters of his time. And one significant thing about him: *He was impatient with the slowness of the mails, and longed for a faster means of communication.* After one of his European visits, he was returning on the ship *Scully* in 1832. Another passenger was Dr. Charles T. Jackson of Boston, one of the pioneers in developing anesthetics. Dr. Jackson happened to say, to a friend, that recent experiments showed that electricity travels extremely fast. Our painter heard that, and said, "If the presence of electricity can be made visible in any part of the circuit, I see no reason why intelligence may not be transmitted instantaneously by electricity."

He worked on his idea for the rest of the voyage. Actually, he knew a little, but *very* little, about electrical phenomena, and little if anything about the various clumsy ideas already tried by others for making an electric telegraph. Not until 1843 did Congress act to finance a telegraph line from Washington to Baltimore. Then, at last, in 1844, Samuel F. B. Morse, ex-painter and inventor of the telegraph and

* John C. Patterson, *America's Greatest Inventors* (New York: Thomas Y. Crowell Company, 1943).

the Morse code, sent his famous message, "What hath God wrought!" Morse still had far to go before his telegraph was accepted and used; and he had many battles to fight in court, defending his patents. But he won out, and died, at eighty-one, a wealthy and honored man.

About six years after Morse sent that message, a young chap named Alfred William Howitt left England for Australia. At thirty-one, he had established himself as an explorer; ". . . he was a steady and intelligent man, an anthropologist, a geologist, and an excellent bushman." I take this description from Allan Moorehead's book,† a superb account of the first expedition across Australia's wasteland. He was a fine leader. Howitt later became a distinguished anthropologist, and a president of the Australian Association for the Advancement of Science. He was chosen, at thirty-one, to lead a rescue party in search of two men. He found them: one dead, the other nearly so. To get any such news back to Melbourne, he had brought carrier pigeons. But when he tried them out, they couldn't fly. They had been carried hundreds of miles on camelback, and had worn off their tail feathers in their small cage. Now, here was a man faced with a problem in which he had had no previous experience; but Howitt met the test. He shot wild pigeons. He tied their tail feathers onto the carrier pigeon stubs, and they flew perfectly! We learn with regret that they never got through: The kites (a form of hawk) picked off the first three; and the fourth, exercising the right to survive, refused to take its chances. So here is Howitt, very much of an all-around man, using great ingenuity in solving a totally new problem.

How did you come out on the Eskimo problem? The solution: *two* men walk to a breathing hole, keeping in step. One stops. The other walks on. The seal hears the other one go on, and thinks the hole is safe.

† *Cooper's Creek* (New York: Dell Publishing Co., 1963).

Did you ever measure the speed of sound? I did. In 1949, our department moved into a new wing, with long halls. A fine echo could be had from the end of a hall on which my lab was situated. One Sunday when alone, I took out my watch and held it so as to read seconds. I practiced a regular clapping of the hands, to make one clap coincide with the echo from the preceding clap. I counted the claps for eighteen seconds. To measure the distance, I paced it off. Simple arithmetic did the rest. Believe it or not, I came to within 2 per cent of the correct value for the speed of sound. Crude? Yes. Were there errors? Certainly. Did some errors happily cancel out, to give such a good answer? I should think so. But: First, I had some fun; second, this venture illustrates what many a scientist or engineer does, in setting up the first experiment to test an idea. Time and again, the first and proper objective is to use the *simplest and most direct means possible to make the desired effect show up at least fairly well*. If it does, *then* further refinement at higher cost, leading to greater accuracy, may be justified.

Undoubtedly, some simple experimental apparatus was first tried at the Nuclear Metals Division of Textron, Inc., when a new process for making spherical metal shot was dreamed up. There are now many uses for various metals in spherical shot form; and with some of the shot so fine it is more nearly a powder. As now developed, there is an electric arc produced between a tungsten electrode which does *not* melt, and the *meltable* electrode made of the desired metal to be made into shot. If only this were done, the melted metal would drip off and splash on the floor. But (and here comes the ingenuity!) the meltable electrode is *rotated*. Fine globules are spun off, surface tension forms them into spheres, and they congeal and harden before they hit the walls of the chamber. All this takes place in an inert gas, so that many kinds of metals, precious or otherwise, can be processed. Ingenious? Very. Simple? Beautifully simple.

Or, consider salt, and the good old salt shaker. Think of how many have tried to improve this ancient device, and with little to no success. And then see what Corning, the famous glass company, did. The container (glass, of course) may be called a little flask. There is a plastic "cork" that has three springy legs: When pushed down into the neck of the flask, they expand, and hold the top in place. The top, or cap, is *notched* all around its edge, to let the salt out. And of course, the whole thing is tastefully designed. Now see what we have here. First, it *works* as a salt shaker. Second, the cap is instantly removable, for cleaning. Third, it is instantly removable for filling. This is ingenuity.

Have you heard of Frederick G. Cottrell? Early in the century, the incomparable Cottrell, a physical chemist, began to give us his process for the electrostatic precipitation of fumes and particles. Every engineer and scientist should read *Cottrell—Samaritan of Science,* by Frank Cameron.‡ Everyone came to "Cot" for help, and one day, in came a man named Buckner Speed. Now, Speed had come up with an admirable idea for getting crude oil from Bakersfield in California down to the coast, where it could be sold to refineries. The ordinary pipeline would not work: this particular oil was just too mean and sticky—it would require too many pumping stations to push it along. This man Speed, you might say, had thought of a way to *lubricate the oil.* He invented the "rifled pipeline": a pipe with grooves in a long spiral. He figured that if he pumped in some *water* along with the oil, the rifling would make the mass rotate; the denser water would be thrown out by centrifugal force to form a water film next to the pipe; and the oil would slide easily along inside this film. How's that for ingenuity?

Speed had first done the right thing: He rigged a small pilot job in his back yard, tested the idea, and it worked. Then four million dollars was raised to build the rifled pipeline. It got the oil to the coast. Then nobody wanted it. The refineries would buy oil with up to around 2 per cent of water in it, but this oil had a lot more than that. Have you

‡ Frank Cameron, *Cottrell—Samaritan of Science* (Garden City, N.Y.: Doubleday & Company, Inc., 1952).

guessed what happened? Every pumping station acted as a mixer—an emulsifier. So Buckner Speed came to Cottrell. Could "Cot" take the water out? "Cot" had never thought of that. But he thought, if electrostatic forces take fumes and particles out of gases, why can't they take water particles out of oil? Here again comes that invaluable ability to throw a simple, preliminary test together, to prove an idea. Cottrell, then and there, put some apparatus together, it worked, and it saved the pipeline project. There were difficulties, however. The scheme worked perfectly for short runs, but not so well at high pressures in long runs, and it was finally given up.

But Cottrell's method for removing water survived. Some wells themselves produce water-loaded oil. As late as 1948, the Cottrell process was de-emulsifying such oil at the rate of half a million barrels per day. As far as I know, it still competes with the chemical processes that also treat such oils.

Could a man, playing with a toy dog, come up with an important aid to space travel? Yes. Theodore Marton of General Electric was working on this problem: An astronaut is out of the ship, at the end of his tether, when he gets into trouble. The pilot must haul him in. But the haul-in, with a flexible line, is uncontrollable, and could be fatal. Marton had a piece of luck. At home, he played with his young son's toy dog, made of beads on strings. With strings *tight,* the strings of beads were *stiff,* and the dog stood. When loose, the dog collapsed. That was the luck of it. Then came ingenuity. In Plate 12, you see Marton's Flexi-Firm Tether. A series of units fit together, ball-and-socket fashion, being strung on a central cable. With a loose cable, you have a rope; tight cable, you have a rigid bar. Please notice that every element of this invention has been with us for many years, and that any number *might* have made the invention. But they *didn't.*

This case sharply points up the fact that there are plenty of inventions yet to be made that do *not* require advanced schooling, refined techniques, soaring off into difficult theories, and so on. Not any of this can ever replace keen interest, keen observation, and ingenuity.

In some of these cases, it may seem as if the ingenious men moved quite directly and naturally to the solutions of their problems. If it so seems, do not take them as typical. We will find as we go along that in the broad sweep of creativity, there is, in the usual case, a rather mysterious break in the path from initial desire to final success. You are a Howitt, out in the wasteland, and your pigeons can't fly. Do you "directly and naturally" think of how to fix them up so they will fly? Typically, you do not. The way the mind works in these affairs is called the *creative process.* Later chapters will gradually get into that.

In the meantime, let me hand you a couple of problems and give you something to think about.

TWO PROBLEMS IN INVENTION

The famed Lord Kelvin invented his extremely simple and fascinating water-dropping electrostatic generator over a century ago. I have built several of these, and have furnished plans to quite a few youngsters around the country. They make their own versions and enter them in science fairs. You will find mine described in my book, *Electrostatics.** One tank of water makes two downward jets of water. The jets break into drops, within rings or collars. These metal rings are cross-connected to a couple of cans lower down, the cans being insulated from each other. Turn it on, and pretty soon, as the charged drops fall into the cans, it builds itself up to about fifteen thousand volts. At this top limit of voltage, the drops have a hard time falling into the cans: They are repelled, they describe beautifully curved paths, and spray all around.

This brought on my dream of making a *ball-dropping* generator, using little metal balls instead of water drops: two streams of balls, dropping in a single file. But how do you manage to make the balls do that? Well, one way is to have a ball tank with a double bottom, with one bottom turning. When a hole in one bottom matches a hole in the other,

* A. D. Moore, *Electrostatics* (Garden City, N.Y.: Doubleday & Company, Inc., 1968).

a ball drops through. Complicated? Yes. So now comes the problem in invention: simplify, by trying to invent a tank-plus-exit that is *fixed*. No moving parts.

Next, we get some *experience*. We get a tin can, and some balls. What balls? Marbles will do, and we can easily get them. We make a hole in the can bottom, or in the side next to the bottom, a little bigger than a marble. We pour in two or three layers of marbles. If we are highly inexperienced and dreadfully optimistic, we think we have it solved. We hope to see the marbles stream out rapidly, one at a time. Of course, nothing of the sort happens. What we have really done is to build a *perfect jamming device* instead of a perfect vending system. In desperation, we pour out all but half a dozen marbles, and tilt the can to get them over the hole. Maybe one drops out, maybe none, maybe two. The others jam. Whereupon, three important things have happened to us.

First, we *failed* to make the invention—which is precisely what happens so often on the first try, and sometimes for many succeeding tries! Second, we have gained some *experience*—and often a lot of that is essential before the breakthrough can ever come. Third, our *stubbornness* is aroused: Are we going to let this little problem send us down to defeat? No sir. Or at least, not until we have given it a good try.

Next, a bit of analysis. That simple hole for an exit permitted jamming—it had no approach—maybe a proper approach, to guide the balls, could be invented, to prevent jamming. In fact, it does appear that there can be no other solution, if indeed there *is* a solution. In the accompanying list, I will give the rigid specifications I am going to impose.

1. Ball diameter, about ¼ inch.
2. Tank: holds one gallon, and is to be, roughly, as wide as it is high.
3. Filling the tank: one gallon of balls is to be *dumped* into the tank.
4. The balls must stream out rapidly, one at a time, and *never* jam.

5. The tank, and the approach to the exit, must be *absolutely static*—with no moving parts, no vibration, no air jets, etc.

This is *my* problem, I made it up, and I will *insist* that all specifications be met.

You may think that my specifications are unreasonable. Why not permit jambreakers that move, in some way, to break up jams? Well, this is merely a sample problem in invention, but the rigid specifications represent what you do encounter in other cases. The laws of nature dictate in any number of ways. Or the needs of your company may dictate. Let's say that your company makes ten devices, all selling at a profit. You invent Device No. 11. It works, and works just fine. But Device No. 11 calls for a pound of platinum, and no substitute. Your company will have to price Device No. 11 at not more than $125. Did you ever look up the cost of a pound of platinum?

In lecturing to any audience on creativity, I always begin by passing out this ball-dropping invention problem. It is a bit shocking to find that in every audience, some highly trained graduate in science or engineering will approach me after the lecture with his "solution": Just put the balls in a long, long tube. Wouldn't they stream out of it rapidly, single-file, and never jam? Certainly. But who gave this fellow the right to violate Specification No. 3? If I were hiring a number of creative scientists and engineers, I would want to test each applicant with a series of invention problems—not to get the problems solved, but to see what *approach* the applicant would use. If an applicant, in most of the problems, jumped the track to violate a specification, I would wish him well, and hope that he would get a job—with my competitor.

By the way, if a certain minister is right, this problem of the balls was solved ages ago. In a book I read, this minister made some kind of moral point by citing the hourglass—which, he said, lets one grain of sand through at a time. If the point he was making is no better than his analogy, he ought to take up some other line of work. The hourglass lets a *stream* of grains through!

The ball-dropping problem again—please note that I have not said that it has been solved, might be solved, or is without a solution. After you have beaten it to death, you may wish to see my comments in the Appendix.

The second invention problem for you comes from the aluminum industry. Before getting to it, go back with me to 1886, to a woodshed behind a clergyman's house in Oberlin, Ohio, and the improvised laboratory of Charles Martin Hall. There in that little laboratory, on February 23, this twenty-two-year-old came through with the electrolytic process for making aluminum. It was one of our great advances. Very oddly, Heroult of France independently made the same discovery at almost the same time. But more: They were born in the same year, and died in the same year.

Aluminum, made by the Hall process, is first cast in heavy bars. These are then drawn, extruded, or rolled into sheets. In making sheets, a thicker sheet becomes thinner and thinner, as it goes between successive rolls. It finally gets down to the *thinnest* sheet the last rolls can make.

But, you say, if they want a still thinner sheet, why not just squeeze down harder on the rolls? Here again, Old Man Experience delights in handing out the hard facts of life. It doesn't work. Why not? Well, when you get to that final stage, the rolls themselves momentarily flatten at the contact areas, and that's that.

The story got to me by word of mouth, and I can't guarantee it in all details. As I heard it, one company realized that if they could only roll the sheet twice as thin, they would have a big market—in the kitchen. As you know, housewives use great quantities of thin aluminum sheet. So there's the problem: Can you invent a way to make that thinnest-rolled sheet, only half as thick as *that*? And *do it very cheaply*. Here is where the *market* imposes a tight specification. Either you price your thin sheet low enough, or it will not sell. This at once rules out any process that might do it at high cost. For example, an electroplating specialist might be able to deplate the sheet electrolytically, to thin it down. For what price? I wouldn't know, but might make a guess at several or many times the price we now pay.

Once, lecturing to a mixed audience in Ottawa, Canada, I passed out this problem, and a housewife solved it before the lecture was over. When you wish to look up the answer, consult the Appendix.

THREE

Keeping Your Creativity Alive

At 17, in 1581, he matriculated as a student in medicine at the University of Pisa. There his constant questioning of the text and lectures held before him made him stand out as an unusual individualist. It also made him unpopular with the more conservative teachers and fellow students.*

Galileo, thus squelched by teachers and fellow students, may give us the first recorded instance of a creative youngster in school being met with impatience.

This book is for you young people. The most important question raised in it is: Why does the high creativity of the child so often disappear before adolescence? Or if maintained to then, die away before maturity? The evidence accumulates to show that a great deal of this is happening. It is a tragedy for the individual and for mankind.

More and more, those who study this wilting away of creativity are drastically criticizing our educational systems that appear to be much to blame for it. We reward the "scholar" with high grades—a scholar being one who can learn the course content and make top marks in examinations. In direct contrast, many teachers have little patience with original thinkers who have ideas of their own.

This chapter goes into these matters, and not only for you.

* Quoted from Bern Dibner and Stillman Drake, *A Letter from Galileo Galilei* (Norwalk, Conn.: Burndy Library, 1967), p. 56.

It will have some things to say to older people—parents, teachers, college professors—that need to be said. And it will suggest ways for you to hold onto your creativity and keep it alive.

VANISHING CREATIVITY

Lewis E. Walkup of the Battelle Memorial Institute is an extremely able researcher and inventor. In a paper on "Individual Creativity in Research,"† he says, "Many attempts have been made to isolate creativity, with little success. It is an almost mystical ability possessed in large measure by gifted people but which most of us exercised as children; exercise now, to a limited extent; and could exercise more effectively if only we appreciated its elements and would practice its development. William N. Sheldon in *Psychology and the Promethean Will* and A. H. Maslow in *Motivation and Personality* have pointed out that most children are highly creative but that, tragically, their creativity vanishes sometime between adolescence and maturity in something Sheldon calls dying back of the brain. This tragedy happens to so great a percentage of mankind that it is scarcely noticed. In fact, the few who escape it are considered a little queer. Fortunately, the few who escape this wilting of mental powers seem to continue to improve their creative abilities up to the onset of senility."

Why does creativity vanish for most of us, and what can be done to preserve and nourish it?

My own feeling is that the demands of life itself account for some of the wilting away. As a child, you had plenty of time to play, to have fun, to keep yourself busy trying things in new ways to get new effects; time to get into mischief; time to be creative in many ways, without even knowing it. As an adolescent, high school keeps you busier, but you are still lighthearted. You get a kick out of making a new pun, or in passing a good one along. You dream up jokes to play on your friends. You help out on the school play. You invent ways to get that scenery assembled and onto that stage, with

† *Battelle Technical Review,* August 1958.

an impossibly small budget to help put it there. Life is still wonderful! And then?

Suddenly, life becomes far more serious. High school is over. You go to work, or you go to college. In either case, your work is pretty well laid out for you, it is demanding, and you have to make good. On the job you work hard, to earn promotion and make enough pay to support a family. Or in college, you concentrate on learning. In either case the demands on you for originality may be few. Is it any wonder that within the very nature of our setup, your creativity languishes, or even dies from neglect?

The break in creativity interest after high school is further marked, these days, by the science fairs. A great many of you who are science-minded are stimulated to do original work in preparing entries for local and regional fairs; and some go on to "national." Having been a judge in a National Science Fair, I know of the fine things many of you have produced. Also, for years, I have responded to requests from young people, in sending plans and instructions of several of my own developments to a good many, from which they have worked up their own variations for these fairs. Good. But then, on a nationwide basis, there is nothing of this sort, at a higher level, in which young people of *college age* can compete in large numbers, and thus keep their creative drives alive.

CREATIVE STUDENTS HAVE TROUBLES

A *Memo to the Faculty from the Center for Research on Learning and Teaching* at my university has this to say: "Not unexpectedly, several sources indicate that the correlation of grades with creative achievement is frequently very low. There is the further argument that the structured constraints of a system of grading have not a neutral but actually a deleterious effect on creative thinking and performance." This *Memo* quotes Dr. Mervin Freedman of San Francisco State College: "Observations indicate that the more creative and individual students tend to be more troublesome to the average teacher than other students.

If the teacher's concern is with order and covering the material, and such a concern may be inevitable in large universities, then someone who gets off the beaten track may get in the way of instruction and be penalized for it by grading, whether the instructor is conscious of such discrimination or not. In other words, the downgrading of creative students, or their failure to achieve good grades, may be a necessary consequence of the various systems involved and may therefore not be susceptible of even the most diligent faculty efforts to control the situation."

So! This says that many of our "brightest" students, as measured by grades, are *not* necessarily our most creative students. Or putting it the other way, our creative students often do not get the high grades. Not only that: *Creative students tend to be somewhat in wrong with their teachers.* Pretty serious situation, don't you think? May not this account for a good deal of the vanishing of creativity between childhood and adolescence, and between that and maturity?

HIGH I.Q. VS. HIGH CREATIVITY

Does high creativity go along with high intelligence? Or is it the other way around, or somewhere in between? Or, putting it into practical form, if your creativity is high but your grades aren't, what is the outlook for you? These questions are simple, but the answers are not. For example, what do we mean by "intelligence"? What do we mean by the "gifted child"? Or the gifted person? Actually, although much research has been done, we know now that much more is needed.

The standard I.Q., or Intelligence Quotient, has long been used as a measure of intelligence. This meaning of intelligence is by no means accepted by all; it is under increasing attack; and I think that in the long run, it may be much modified. Meantime, it is still with us, and will be, for some time to come. It is often supplemented by other tests, such as a test for creativity.

An extremely interesting piece of research by Getzels and Jackson, of the University of Chicago, compares the highly

intelligent with the highly creative adolescent.‡ They tested
449 adolescents in a Midwestern private secondary school,
both for I.Q., and creativity. Of course, they found a wide
range of mixtures: some high in both; some low in both; some
high in one and low in the other, and vice versa.

From these, they were able to pick out two groups of about
equal size (twenty-six in one, twenty-eight in the other).
The I.Q. group had individuals who were all in the top 20
per cent in I.Q., but all were *below* the top 20 per cent in
creativity. The other, or creative group, had individuals who
were all in the top 20 per cent in creativity, but all were *below* the top 20 per cent in I.Q. These two groups were then
further studied in certain ways. Here are some of the findings.

Fantasy. When required to write a story about a stimulus
picture, there was a striking difference between the two
groups. The I.Q. group tended to be conventional, stodgy.
The creatives made significantly greater use of stimulus-
free themes, unexpected endings, incongruities, and play-
fulness; they had imagination, and they turned it loose.

Occupational Preference. Those who made the study
rated occupations such as doctor, engineer, businessman
as "conventional." Occupations such as inventor, artist,
spaceman, disc jockey, they rated as "unconventional."
Only 18 per cent of the I.Q. group went unconventional
in their choice of occupations. However, 62 per cent of the
creatives did.

Sense of Humor. They were all asked to consider eight
qualities, such as character, sense of humor, etc., and to rank
themselves in the order in which they would like to be outstanding. Here comes a dramatic difference. The I.Q. group
put sense of humor at the bottom. The creatives put it second
from top!

Teacher Attitude. The teachers were asked to rate these
students on the degree to which they enjoyed having them
in class, as compared with the *whole* student population.
Again, it was clear-cut. The teachers found the I.Q. group

‡ *Scientific Creativity: Its Recognition and Development* (New
York: John Wiley & Sons, 1963), Chap. 13.

more desirable than the average students. They found the creatives *less* desirable than the average students.

What a bearing this has on the phenomenon of vanishing creativity! We find here that the highly creative adolescent tends to have more fantasy, more imagination; tends to unconventional occupational preferences; tends to have a high sense of humor (and no doubt gets in wrong by exercising it, having a greater capacity for mischief-making!); and tends to let unconventional attitudes show up enough to earn some disapproval from the teachers.

In short, creativity doesn't need to wait until adolescence is over to start the vanishing act. Subtle disapproval, and sometimes positive squelching, can begin to strangle it to death during adolescence itself. Teachers, parents, counselors, take note! Isn't it about time for us to be giving creativity a break?

As for you, my creative young friend, you can read. You have read the foregoing. You know that unless you are lucky, the cards may be stacked somewhat against you. If you are made of the right stuff, you won't sag down and quit. Instead, it will add to your backbone, your determination. On the one hand, you *could* try a little harder to fit more gracefully into this conventional old world of ours. But on the other, you will go right ahead practicing creativity on your own. Let no man squelch your sense of humor: You will need it! Let nothing cramp your imagination: You'll need it! After all, this will not be the first time the cards are stacked against you. Just wait until you are up against some real project, some day in your future—and it may seem, for a while, that everything is stacked against you. Which, of course, will just make you all the more stubborn.

THE FAILURE OF THE COLLEGES

Those who speak for education in higher institutions often put it this way: You are in college, not so much to learn, as to *learn how to learn*. Or again, they often say that the mission of higher education is to teach you *how to think*.

There is some truth in both of these noble statements. As to science and engineering, I wish I could say that these educational areas also have, as a main purpose, the stimulation of your creativity, and that they succeed in doing it. I am afraid that neither is true. In fact, I suspect that the taking of a degree in engineering or science may, in many cases, do more to stifle creativity than to stimulate it.

This is a very serious charge, it needs support, and I hereby support it.

As to *learning* in science or engineering, there is a great deal to be learned, with more asking to be added to the content every day. You are kept so everlastingly busy at learning that there is little time to be creative. Knowledge, of course, is essential to the creative process; but knowledge is not creation. Solving assigned problems does call for some creativity. But if there is no time for practicing creativity "on your own," it won't be practiced. Every faculty feels that a certain large content *must* be crammed in. Every faculty member is under pressure to see that his course covers the ground.

In spite of these pressures, there are two possibilities for stimulating creativity that might be used. I am afraid that very largely we fail at both. What are these possibilities?

First, your college textbooks: In presenting you with theorems, proofs, principles, devices, machines, circuits, reactions, or whatever, the textbook *could* be a prime source of inspiration. How? By at least occasionally lapsing into a bit of history and biography, to tell you how this theorem defied everyone for centuries, until a certain man proved it; or how this other fellow worked for ten years before he made his breakthrough; and so on. Do your textbooks of today do this sort of thing? With rare exceptions, they do not. I invite any doubters to take a look at them. I have.

Second, your college instructors could be prime sources of inspiration. Even allowing for the pressures under which they work, they could certainly take a little time, once in a while, to fill this gap with interesting and pertinent examples of discoveries and inventions, and a bit about the men who made them. They could; but with rare exceptions, they do not. In fact, as far as I can sense, most faculty members have little interest in creativity, and know even less about it.

Which, you see, puts it again squarely up to you. Is there anything you can do, after high school, to nourish your own creative interests? There certainly is. You can read. No matter how busy you think you are, you can read autobiography, biography, accounts of famous discoverers and inventors, and so on. One such book or paper leads to another. A lot of it is heady, exciting stuff. Beyond that, you can adopt several long-time projects of your own, to learn about as odd times permit, and to think about, on the run. They might never come through, but they will keep you in practice; and a lot of valuable learning will stick to you in the process.

DO HIGH COLLEGE GRADES INDICATE HIGH CREATIVITY?

Another significant study presented in the book, *Scientific Creativity*, was made by Taylor and Ghiselin. There were 239 engineering graduates studied in an engineering research center. Such centers usually recruit from the top fourth of the graduating class. In this center, personnel shortages caused by World War II forced the hiring of men from anywhere in the class, just so they had engineering degrees. Their later research success was given a merit rating in terms of top, second, and third levels of performance. It was found that the college grades had no relation whatever to later research success.

More such studies are needed, and one may hope that the impact of this one will cause others to be made. As far as we can now predict, they may give much the same answer.

So now, consider the creative youngster who may never be an honor student. If he is a keen observer, crammed full of imagination and curiosity and persistence, he might rank anywhere in his class in school or college, and yet turn out to have the highest lifetime creative record.

PRACTICE

The continued practice of a talent makes it grow. Lack of practice lets it wither away. I shall never forget a young Russian I knew, years ago, with a superb voice. He was a "natural." As a college student, and without training, his stage presence and his solo performances were at a level that others attain only after several years of hard work. A splendid career would open up for him, if. . . . But the "if" won out. It was all too easy for him. He scorned advice. He was soon lost from view. Practice was beneath him, you see. I doubt if he felt he could learn something from anyone else. In contrast, a friend of ours, Marilyn Mason, one of the world's finest organists, always maintains her practice. We are often in her home, where she has a baby pipe organ, for home practice. And when did she begin practice at the piano? At age six. Soon, she took to the organ. And she has never stopped practicing.

I had always yearned to juggle, but never could. Then, in middle life, I saw a famous juggler. He bestirred my yearnings, I bought three rubber balls, and started in. For two weeks, nothing much happened but chasing dropped balls, and collecting a mass of very sore muscles. At last, a little bit of a breakthrough came along. It felt like a great triumph. Even so, that little bit of progress had to be followed by thousands and thousands of passes before any real, versatile facility was gained. Practice!

Likewise for creativity. No matter how busy you are on the job or in college, you can keep your eye sharpened for things needing improvement, and for unusual effects, whatever they may be. Or if you like to write verse, you can keep those talents alive by *writing* it—and then everlastingly improving it until it is *good*.

And again, there are these longtime projects you can adopt, returning to one or another from time to time. As you learn, in your courses or by your reading, one of them may be demolished. And so be it—you can't always win. But another project may pick up some encouragement, and look better.

True enough, you may adopt a project that is far ahead of you at the time: But it, or some offshoot from it, may come ripe for you a decade later. *Having your mind on it means that anything learned that bears on it, is all the more easily and permanently learned.* Later on, you will hear about John Alby Spencer, and how he kept that mind of his on a goal!

A type of creativity we might call the adaptation game can be played by anyone, almost any time, anywhere. This involves picking up an object, made for a definite purpose, and seeing how many other uses you can think of for it. Consider the Eastman Kodak Company, where a great many creative minds are needed. They have a ten-week course for technicians and executives, and in it, there is a two-week home assignment. Each man gets a "creativity kit" (called a "junk box") having string, pieces of cardboard, sticks, buttons, safety pins, and whatnot. The objective is to *make* something. A prime purpose is to jar a man loose from his mental blocks, free his mind, get him out of ruts and dead-end traps: Turn him into a flexible thinker. A mind thus shaken loose and made free-wheeling may, on the job, consider and devise new ways of doing things around the plant.

Going back to the adopt-a-project idea, a prime advantage can be illustrated by my present project, writing this book. It is forever and always on my mind, either actively, or lurking in the background. So what happens? In my general reading, I am constantly finding items of interest to creativity in one way or another, without even looking for them. They seem to jump out of the page! Likewise, your longtime project will make you come alert every time your reading of a newspaper, magazine, book, or advertisement has anything at all to say that can add to your knowledge in your selected area. Five or ten years from now, you may almost be a specialist in the project's category.

A BIT OF GLASS

In that glass plant where I roamed freely as a child, a kindly glassworker gave me one of my most vividly remembered experiences. He got a blob of red-hot glass on the end of a rod. Together, we walked to a large bowl of water. He dropped that blob into the water. Now hear this: He had one hand immersed, and he caught that hot blob in his hand—and manipulated it! Do you wonder that I remember it? But wait. When it was cold, he brought it out and handed it to me. It had a smooth, rounded body, with a tail that ended in a very fine tip. He told me to grasp the body in my hand. I did. The tail stuck out. He pinched off the end of the tail. I felt a jolt. I opened my hand. Powder. Nothing in it but glass powder! Can you explain it? And if so, as a young creative, could you keep working at it until you make an invention out of it?

If you are widely read, wide awake to a lot of developments, have a mind that works faster than mine, and are possibly lucky to boot, you would stop me right here and say, "That invention has already been made!" Right. It has been.

But first, the name of these glass pollywogs: Prince Rupert's Tears. It is an old trick, centuries old, no doubt. The water chilled and set the outer skin, *after* which the molten interior began to cool. As the interior cooled, it *shrank,* thus pulling inward on the skin, and *compressing* it. High internal stresses were set up. Break that tail, the stresses take over at terrific speed, and the pollywog fractures itself into tiny bits.

Now for the invention: *tempered glass.* Tempered glass, treated as above, but less violently, is heated, then skin-chilled. It has two outstanding properties. First, it is extremely strong. Second, if struck a hard but highly localized blow, the whole pane shatters into small, not-very-sharp fragments—instead of into long, dangerous shards. Well, isn't that just what you would like to have in the windows (except for the windshield) in your family car? You have!

Tempered glass might have come along years before it actually did. That was long after I had that handful of glass powder to tell you about.

Keep your creativity alive. You might today see some interesting but old trick or phenomenon or process or happening. Get it on your mind, possibly experiment with it, and come up with an entirely new and valuable adaptation of it.

FOUR

Creative People: What Are They Like?

A bit of our folklore has it that inventors are often slightly off the beam; or, shall we say, a bit wacky. One of our sayings is, "You don't have to be crazy to be an inventor, but it helps."

An even stronger thread running through our culture derives from movies, television series, and some science fiction stories in which the main character is a cold-blooded, malevolent scientist, bent on destroying mankind. He is smarter than all of those who contend against his creative magic. As often as not, he is demented. Such fool ideas do the cause of creativity no good. Dr. Lawrence S. Kubie has shown in his book* that mental illness blocks creativity.

To help erase the wacky inventor concept, I am going to tell you about a number of creative men; first, about a number it has been my good fortune to meet or know, and then, some others. If you are not already an avid reader of biography, perhaps hearing about some of these characters will get you started.

CREATIVE MEN AS REAL PEOPLE

Go back with me to Carnegie Tech around 1912, and a professor I had there, C. J. Davisson. As a lecturer, he had all the weak points. He was a wispy little nervous man with a prominent Adam's apple, and a stammer. But we respected

* *Neurotic Distortions of the Creative Process* (New York: Farrar, Straus & Giroux, Inc., 1963).

him. Later, at Bell Telephone Laboratories, he worked with electron diffraction, and discovered that electrons can behave like waves. Sir George Thomson also made the discovery in England, and in 1937 they shared a Nobel Prize in Physics. Sir George, in a delightful book,† pays high tribute to Davisson, telling us that he did much of his laboratory work with his own hands, and that everyone loved him. "He had a delightful sense of humor and was full of quiet fun, sometimes unexpected." In Plate 5 you see his co-worker L. H. Germer seated, with Davisson facing him.

In sharp contrast, consider my towering Australian friend, Douglas Lampard. A leading professor of electrical engineering in Australia, head of his department; and he likes nothing better than to play in a hot jazz band. Some years ago, Lampard used a lot of tough mathematics to solve a special case of electrical capacitance, and got the answer. Encouraged, he tackled another special case. But this one was so tough that he had to use a computer. Surprise: Same answer as for the first case! Could a general law be declaring itself? He went on, developed the general proof for what became Lampard's Theorem; and beyond that, out of it came a new and highly accurate electrical standard.

Gary Muffly, one of my early students, came to mind some years back when we were at our Canadian cabin in the Blind River area. A most exciting mystery had broken loose. Core drills and teams were being flown into the bush. Prospectors from all over were flocking in and roaming the rocky forests. The air was thick with rumor. Planes were endlessly sweeping overhead, back and forth. Suddenly, the biggest claim-staking operation ever attempted took place. Only then did we learn that we were on the edge of one of the greatest uranium discoveries: the Elliot Lake uranium strike. And those planes overhead? Some were making magnetic surveys, using the flux-gate magnetometer; and Gary Muffly was one of its inventors. You would take him to be an extremely sober man, but I know better; he has an owlish sense of humor. And recently at Gulf Research Corporation

† *The Inspiration of Science* (New York: Oxford University Press, 1961).

near Pittsburgh, he showed me his fantastic gravity meter, and described its accuracy. If you were to set it on the floor of the Washington Monument and adjust it, then carry it up to any step and set it down, and tell him the reading, he would tell you what step it is on.

Accuracy brings the gyroscope to mind and its inventor, Elmer A. Sperry. His gyroscope first made accurate navigation possible. Years ago, several of us had the pleasure of sitting down and talking with him in New York, before a banquet started. A grand old fellow. Charming, courteous, full of good humor. He and Edison were great pals in those days, so I asked him if Edison was really as deaf as was generally supposed. "Yes," said Sperry, "he's as deaf as a post in one ear, and you have to expectorate in the other!"

The most gracious host I ever had was when, at another time in New York, I was the dinner guest of Michael Pupin at the University Club. His amazing life story is told in his book, *From Immigrant to Inventor*. Young Michael came from Serbia at sixteen, with five cents in his pocket. He was immediately skinned out of the five cents. There is so much I would like to tell about him (you *must* read his book!) A man of great strength, he became president of his class at Columbia University (where a physics laboratory is named for him); for many years, he was a famed Columbia professor. He was the first to make X rays in America; the first to intensify the plate by using a fluorescent screen next to it (supplied by Edison); the first to make an X-ray exposure that was followed by surgery; and renowned for inventing the loading coils that extended the distance for making telephone calls. A charming man, universally honored and beloved.

Back in that era there was a genius who did have his oddities, but you might too, if likewise handicapped. This was the electrical wizard of General Electric, Charles Proteus Steinmetz, a hunchback. Famed for his electrical contributions, and equally famed for his ever-present cigar. His favorite recreation was to get out alone in his canoe, for paddling, and thinking. It was by way of the Steinmetz cigar that I had the luck of meeting him. There was a technical meeting in Pittsburgh when I was in college; he was to attend; and I went, just to see him. I sat behind and to one side, and made a pencil sketch of the great man. Came an intermission, and I stepped out on the entrance landing. I saw Steinmetz coming. I had my matches ready. He whipped out his cigar, I lighted it for him, and so had the thrill of meeting Steinmetz.

General Electric of course was where Irving Langmuir, one of our most creative scientists, carved out his career. One of my regrets is that on visiting his laboratory, I did not get to meet him. But on that trip, I made a special point of visiting Ernst F. W. Alexanderson, who made fine contributions in many electrical areas. A most genial man he was. As to invention, he contributed 313 patents, having taken out, on the average, a patent every seven weeks for forty-six years.

In those days, a young fellow who never went to college was learning things by working for Langmuir. He became the first to do cloud seeding with silver iodide. My friend Vincent J. Schaefer is now one of our best-known scientists. He is now Director of the Atmospheric Sciences Research Center at Albany. He is a man (Plate 15) of many interests, highly creative, and blessed with a grand sense of humor.

A memory I cherish came from giving a fluid mapper demonstration for R.C.A. at Princeton. I was already started and was booming along, when a man arrived late. The short little man quietly found a seat. I had never seen him, but had seen pictures. I stopped short, grinned at him, and said, "Are you Zworykin?" "Yes," said he, and grinned back. He, of course, is the famed inventor of the iconoscope and other items that made TV possible.

Jim Lafferty comes to mind next (Plate 16). He was another early student of mine, a big man with a ready laugh. He and his group at General Electric recently made a historic breakthrough. The effort to make a heavy-current interrupter in a sealed vacuum started thirty-five years before, but it was years ahead of its time. Lafferty and his group, using new materials, and with a huge amount of research, brought it off. Lafferty has taken out fifty-four patents.

John Kraus, another of my students, grew up in my city of Ann Arbor. As a boy, he was crazy about radio, and had antennas sprouting from the yard and housetop. Along with his books and his work in radio astronomy, he is known the world over for inventing the spiral antenna.

The only true genius I ever had among thousands of students was Gabriel Kron. Short, heavy, always amiable, brilliant, and with ordinary arithmetic often beyond him. Impatient with lowly arithmetic, perhaps? In his later years he wrote mathematical papers so advanced that some had to be sent abroad to be reviewed by the few able to read them.

Another brilliant student I had was very quiet: Claude Shannon, who became the expert in information theory. Though sober, he has his little ways. He and Professor Minsky of M.I.T. invented that fascinating little box. It has a closed lid. There is a button in front. You push the button. The lid rises. A little arm reaches up and out and over. The hand pushes the button. The arm retreats, the lid shuts down, and you view all this with the feeling that somehow, you have lost an argument.

In 1939 at a banquet in Ann Arbor, I had the good fortune to be seated next to a very personable young chap of twenty-nine who was already on his way to fame and fortune. I had a good long talk with this college dropout. After a freshman year at Harvard, he quit, to perfect his first invention; and he never finished college. He now holds over two hundred patents. Discoveries, he says, are made "by some individual who has freed himself from a way of thinking that is held by friends and associates who may be more intelligent, better eduacted, better disciplined, but who have not mastered the art of the fresh, clean look at the old, old knowledge." He himself often spends prolonged periods working on projects in his plant's laboratory. *Fortune* magazine says that he and his wife are worth over half a billion dollars. This is Edwin H. Land, inventor of Polaroid, and maker of Polaroid cameras.

—AND SOME OTHERS

Can a self-seeking scalawag be creative? He certainly can be, and Count Rumford proved it to the hilt. Sanborn C. Brown's book, *Count Rumford*,‡ gives a fascinating account of this twisted, gifted man. Born in New England in 1753 as James Thompson, he turned against his country and became a cynical soldier of fortune. He carved out a remarkable career in Europe. He was a great organizer, experimenter, and prolific inventor. His work in heat and ballistics helped to found modern physics. He perfected the fireplace; and, away back then, he invented the kitchen stove and the drip coffeepot.

In direct contrast, turn to William Thomson, later Lord Kelvin—upright, honest, universally respected, who lived a long and extremely productive life as mathematician, theorist, experimenter, inventor, engineer. Among his many contributions, what he did to make the Atlantic Cable possible would alone secure his place among famous men. D. K. C. MacDonald's fine book, *Faraday, Maxwell, and Kelvin*,* covers his life and works.

Michael Faraday, our greatest experimenter, had the gift of keen physical insight, coupled with the ability to invent experiments for testing theories, and a great capacity of constructing the apparatus for the experiments. He was a superb elucidator, both in his writings and his lectures. A most lovable man.

James Clerk Maxwell: He took the concepts and experimental findings of Faraday, whom he greatly respected, and with his keen analytical mind developed electromagnetic theory in the form known as the famed Maxwell's Equations. And was he therefore a pure theorist? Far from it. MacDonald tells us of how Maxwell, as a small child, delighted his parents by everlastingly pestering them to ex-

‡ Sanborn C. Brown, *Count Rumford* (Garden City, N.Y.: Doubleday & Company, Inc., 1962).

* D. K. C. MacDonald, *Faraday, Maxwell, and Kelvin* (Garden City, N.Y.: Doubleday & Company, Inc., 1964).

plain every device in and around the house. He too was an experimenter and builder of instruments. He wrote fine poetry, and had a keen sense of humor. Like Faraday, he was universally beloved.

The oddest genius to appear in this book had rather extreme peculiarities. He had an acute phobia about germs, and was forever washing his hands, ". . . for every reason and no reason. . . ." Hotel waiters were used to him. "A fresh tablecloth at every meal and two dozen clean napkins was his standing order. Although the silverware had been sterilized at his request, he was still compelled to clean each piece personally with a clean napkin before he could use it. He could not tolerate a fly, and if one should light upon his table, this would bring a demand for the removal of everything. Then the meal would be started all over again." These quotations, taken from *Lightning in his Hand*,† do not by any means complete the picture of his oddities. This was Nikola Tesla, a man whose mind was able to take great intuitive leaps. By inventing the three-phase induction motor and extending the use of alternating current, he made great contributions.

America's greatest inventor, Thomas Alva Edison, was one of the busiest men who ever lived. He was simply phenomenal. Matthew Josephson's biography, *Edison*,‡ wonderfully well portrays the man and his career. Like all of us, Edison made some mistakes in judgment, but they were few. He had very unusual foresight. He saw that his electric generators, alone, would get him nowhere, no matter how good they were. Therefore, he went ahead to develop an entire electrical *system* by which he could not only produce power, but also get it to his customers. It is commonly thought that Edison invented the incandescent lamp. He didn't. Others had such lamps before him, but they were no good. When Edison set out to *improve* the lamp, he used the newly invented Sprengel vacuum pump; and then he

† Inez Hunt and Wanetta W. Draper, *Lightning in his Hand* (Denver, Colorado: Sage Books, 1964).

‡ Matthew Josephson, *Edison* (New York: McGraw-Hill Book Company, 1959).

displayed his enormous capacity for working, working, and keeping on working. He tried hundreds and hundreds of ways to make the filament before he got one that, for those days, was pretty good. Thus, he was the man who invented the *improvements* that made the lamp a success. Nowadays many, who ought to know better, look down their noses at Edison for what they describe as his "blind experimentation." They forget, or do not know, that many of his inventions were, at that time, long leaps into the unknown. There was much of science yet to be developed. Either you went ahead on your own, as best you could, or you went nowhere. Edison always went ahead. His patents testify to that: 1093 patents, the largest number ever granted to an American.

A. J. Musselman was an inveterate inventor who enjoyed life to the full. When there wasn't enough fun to be had, he would invent some. One of the most hilarious little books you can come across is *Wheels in his Head*, by his son, M. M. Musselman.* "A.J." had an infinite capacity for dreaming up stunts and getting into trouble as a small boy, and he never let up. One night, someone broke into Musselman's bike shop in Wichita, Kansas, stole an expensive bike, and headed west. "A.J.," being a prize-winning bike racer himself, mounted his racing bike and gave chase. For six hundred miles he followed the trail, from town to town. Some days later, beyond Colorado Springs, up at Cripple Creek, he gave up, turned around, and started down the Rocky Mountain slope. Faster and faster. Then, too fast. He braked with his shoe against the front tire, until he got the world's hottest hot foot. He had to ditch. Another try, same story: He ditched again. Then he cut brush to drag behind him, and made it down the slope. And what came of this wild ride? Some years later, he became the inventor of the coaster brake. Some of his many other inventions also panned out. His most important invention was the soft tire—the large, underinflated tire that made it possible for airplanes to land.

* M. M. Musselman, *Wheels in his Head* (New York: McGraw-Hill Book Company, 1945).

FROM BOREDOM TO INVENTION

My Canadian paper has just told me that Clarence B. Darrow, seventy-eight, has died. In the 1930s Darrow was a stove salesman and heating engineer. The Depression was on, and time hung heavy on his hands. So he thought up a game, made the parts by hand, and began playing it with friends. It caught on locally, and he turned out sets for more friends—at first, two a day.

At a hundred sets, production went beyond Darrow's facilities. He approached toy manufacturers, but was turned down. "They told me that there were too many players in the game, that it was too complicated, that it took too long, and that it would end up in families fighting each other." (Thus, the verdict of the experts!) So, he set up to produce the game himself and to sell it, store to store. When he got up to twenty thousand sets a year, Parker Brothers, the largest game manufacturer, made a deal with him. A few years ago, Darrow estimated his royalties at a million dollars, and the money was still rolling in.

What game? "Monopoly." It is the biggest thing that ever hit the game business. And the experts had turned it down.

This case deserves comment. First, here was a man whose background (sales, stoves, heating) did not point to game invention. But second, he could not stay idle (creative people are *busy* people, not idlers). Third, the game experts had *four* "good" reasons for "knowing" that his crazy game could never catch on. Fourth, he had faith in himself: He went right ahead on his own, demonstrated a commercial success, and proved the experts wrong.

I wish I could tell you how to invent a million-dollar game. I can't. No one can. No one can predict public acceptance of a game. Which brings a challenge to you. With your creativity, if you could work up an analysis of successful games that would take only a goodly part out of the guesswork of predicting, you could name your own salary.

TEAM WORKER OR LONER?

In the spring of 1941 I was asked to work part-time for the Naval Ordnance Laboratory, to find and hire creative younger and older scientists and engineers. We were not yet in World War II, but they were certain we would be. The laboratory was under great pressure to build up personnel, to work on magnetic mines, degaussing of ships, and many other projects. In a few months I was able to hire 150 men for the laboratory.

During one of my trips to Washington, the head of one laboratory project took me to a large room. Over here were five or six men, working as a team. Over there, by himself, was Blank (let's call him that)—one of my own graduates. My friend indicated Blank, and quietly said, "Blank would be of much greater value to us, if I could only get him to work in a team." You would never see a more clear-cut case of its kind, all in one big room: the team here, the loner over there; all under pressure to produce desperately needed equipment—and the boss there to render that judgment. *Was his judgment correct?*

Now consider another case: A. A. Michelson. Born on the German-Polish frontier in 1872, Michelson was brought to America at the age of two, graduated from our Naval Academy, and became an instructor there in chemistry and physics. While at the Academy, A. A. Michelson constructed some apparatus for about ten dollars, with which he measured the velocity of light with the highest accuracy yet attained. Eventually, the newly endowed University of Chicago called him, knowing that he would attract graduate students. He did. But he soon found that working with them interfered with his research, and he would have none of it. He called in another very able man (we come to him next) to take this "burden" off his hands. Moreover, Michelson would not attend faculty meetings, nor take on administrative duties.

Michelson, working alone, devised better apparatus, with which he measured the speed of light in a vacuum. Then came his masterpiece: Using the interferometer he had invented at age twenty-two, he attacked the stationary ether theory, and found no effect of the drift of the earth through the supposed ether. Here was a landmark contribution, by a loner, if there ever was one. As you know, he was the first American to receive the Nobel Prize in Physics. Bernard Jaffe tells you all about him in *Michelson and the Speed of Light.*†

Robert Millikan was the man Michelson called in to handle those graduate students. Young Millikan had been a *classical* scholar at Oberlin, graduated, and was then pressed into service there to teach—what?—*physics!* Later, he took work at Columbia (some under Michael Pupin) and in Europe. Michelson cabled him in Europe, to come to Chicago. Those graduate students that Michelson didn't want kept Millikan busy, and he did not seriously turn to research until he was nearly forty! He was the first to turn the cloud chamber into a droplet chamber; and later, to use oil droplets instead of water. He demonstrated for the first time that electrons, one by one, got onto a droplet; and of course, he went on to measure the electron charge. His photoelectric experiments, of equal or greater importance, added luster, and his Nobel Prize marks him as one of our greats.

Millikan was a team worker. Not in the sense that he ever needed any help from anyone except instrument makers; but he got along splendidly with graduate students and all others. A young Millikan of today, on joining a large firm, would soon be in a research team, and soon be running it. In a short while his genius would be recognized, and he would be given his own head, to work as he pleased.

Millikan should remind us of Albert E. Hull of General Electric, the world's most prolific inventor of electron tubes (and Lafferty's boss for fourteen years, by the way). Hull majored in Greek, and taught Greek, French, and German. But at last, a physics course he once took caught up with his interests, and he joined Willis R. Whitney's laboratory

† Bernard Jaffe, *Michelson and the Speed of Light* (New York: Doubleday & Company, Inc., 1960).

staff. Hull: from Greek to electron tubes. Millikan: from the classics to a Nobel Prize in Physics.

Going back to young Blank at Naval Ordnance: Was his boss right? I never knew, for I lost track of him. But the point is that when a true loner comes along, like Michelson, he is, and will remain, a loner.

Perhaps you are a bit curious as to which I am? When I started teaching at the University of Michigan in 1916, there was no talk of team research. That wasn't heard of until years later. Faculty members in most engineering colleges were under no pressure to do research, as they are today. I chose to experience the joys of research and discovery as an individual. I have always wanted to pioneer, instead of following the crowd. In that sense, I am a loner. But I like people. I enjoy working with them when they bring their problems to me. When I do make some advance, I have a tremendous urge to share the excitement with others—and in that sense am by no means a loner. Also, I have strong design inclinations, and strong desires for making things myself. I want, as far as I can, to see a project all the way through—from invention, through development, to design, to making it, and then publishing a paper on it and lecturing on it. Many people come to my laboratory. If the manager of some research institute dropped in and saw all of the apparatus I have built myself, he would think I should not use my time that way. If I worked for him, he would discourage it. But you see, I don't have to work for him. Thus, we are both happy.

SO THEN: WHAT ARE CREATIVE PEOPLE LIKE?

After reading about these creative specimens, could you write a theme about "The Personal Characteristics of the Creative Man"? Pretty difficult. Creative talent resides in men of all shapes and sizes and dispositions. Some are theoretical, living the life of the mind; some are physical, preferring real things, and experimentation. Some are both.

But they do have some qualities pretty much in common. They observe. They are intuitive. They are imaginative.

They have "drive": They are very busy people. A large proportion have a good sense of humor—which recalls to us how those adolescents in the creative group gave a sense of humor such a high rating.

I can't resist adding one more to the group: Sir Charles Vernon Boys, who long since wrote a famous book, *Soap Bubbles.* (It is reprinted in the Science Study Series.) Many people I run into have enjoyed it. Boys made some notable contributions, one being to measure the gravitational constant so accurately that his value stood for fifty years. What was he like? He had fun. When he made a discovery, they all knew it: He would come out of his laboratory whooping and yelling, and leaping over tables and chairs. What I like best is his giant smoke ring generator. His window overlooked the walk below, and he installed his generator there. When an innocent passerby came along, Sir Charles would ring him with one of his big smoke doughnuts. Isn't that just wonderful?

Now that we have admired some ingenious men and their products, isn't it time that we asked some of them to tell us, as best they could in their own words, how they did it?

FIVE

What Creative Men Have Said

Fortunately, some discoverers and inventors have reviewed their experiences and told, as nearly as they could, how it was with them: what happened in their creative processes. If this is your first time at reading such statements, you are in for a surprise.

How many of your teachers have ever told you to welcome intuition, or to "play a hunch"? Several? Two? One? None? Probably, none.

Now, creative men have found that their contributions do not come from knowledge alone, or reasoning alone, or through routine combinations of these, no matter how good the routines are. A great deal of your schooling is concerned with acquiring knowledge, skills, and routines, and learning how to reason. These are necessary for the creative act, *but not sufficient*. Furthermore, these can be acquired outside of school. (They *were* acquired by one who had only a few months of schooling, Thomas Alva Edison.)

School, then, is necessary for most of us; but nearly everywhere, at any level, it is concerned with learning, and hardly at all concerned with creativity. Usually, a mysterious but vital stage or step in the creative process gets anywhere from little to no emphasis in the school experience.

FROM GOLDSMITH, LANGMUIR, EINSTEIN

We first hear from Dr. Alfred N. Goldsmith, pioneer in radio, TV, and motion pictures.

GOLDSMITH: Creativeness, to venture a crude definition, is the production and disclosure of a new fact, law, relationship, device or product, process or system based generally on available knowledge but not following directly, easily, simply, or even by usual logical processes from the guiding information at hand. A possible explanation of creativeness is that it is based on intuitive processes.

That is from "Creativity: A Symposium," *IRE Student Quarterly* (September 1957), a part of which Goldsmith wrote. He quotes Einstein:

EINSTEIN: I believe in intuition and inspiration. . . . At times I feel certain I am right while not knowing the reason. . . . Imagination is more important than knowledge. For knowledge is limited, whereas imagination embraces the entire world, stimulating progress, giving birth to evolution. It is, strictly speaking, a real factor in scientific research.

Goldsmith continues, with Irving Langmuir:

LANGMUIR: In the complicated situations of life, we have to solve numerous problems and make many decisions. It is absurd to think that reason should be our guide in all cases. Reason is too slow and too difficult. We do not have the necessary data or we cannot simplify our problem sufficiently to apply the methods of reasoning. What then must we do? Why not do what the human race has always done—use the abilities we have—our common sense, judgment, and experience. We underrate the importance of intuition. In almost every scientific problem which I have succeeded in solving, even after those that have taken days or months of work, the final solution has come to my mind in a fraction of a second by a process which is not consciously one of reason. Such intuitive ideas are often wrong. The good must be sorted out from the bad—sometimes by common sense or judgment—other times by reasoning. The power of the human mind is far more remarkable than one ordinarily thinks.

Vincent J. Schaefer also tells about Langmuir, under whom he trained, in his paper, "Can We Do It Better?"*

SCHAEFER: Langmuir emphasized the futility of making formal plans in an effort to obtain new ideas. He stressed the importance of developing a receptive mind which could accept a new idea engendered by a fortunate accident, an unexpected occurrence or some other set of circumstances generally beyond the control of the individual thus benefited.

Let's pause here to see what Langmuir meant. We have been working hard, theorizing and experimenting, and trying to explain this new effect we are getting. We need a new idea, which may come out to be a new law, or relationship, or whatever. We are well-informed. We know logic. We know reason. So we say to ourselves, let's stop fooling around, and sit down at this desk and reason straight through to the answer. Did Langmuir say that? He did not. He said that this is the very process that will not work. Note that he spoke of underrating the importance of intuition. Another name for intuition is hunch. Is Langmuir really telling us to pay attention to that hunch? Yes, he is. And you read, from Einstein, "I believe in intuition and inspiration. . . . Imagination is more important than knowledge."

But hold on. Are they then saying that the way to discover a new law or make a brilliant invention, is to wait until the right hunch comes along—and thereby avoid a lot of lost time and hard work? No. Nearly always, we have to *earn* that hunch, that intuition, that inspiration, by a lot of dedicated preliminary work.

* *Bulletin of the American Meteorological Society* (February 1968).

John K. Williams, in *The Wisdom of Your Subconscious Mind*,† refers to some famous creatives:

HELMHOLTZ: [After previous investigations of a problem] . . . in all directions . . . happy ideas come unexpectedly without effort, like an inspiration. So far as I am concerned they have never come to me when my mind is fatigued or when I was at my working table. [Helmholtz got his inspirations when rested—often in the morning.]

EDISON: The key to successful methods comes right out of the air. A real, new thing like an idea, a beautiful melody, is pulled out of space.

POINCARÉ: . . . creative ideas did not come to him while he worked at his desk, but frequently flashed into his mind while engaged in other activities.

A study of 1450 research chemists is cited by Williams. A large share of major chemical advances of the preceding thirty years had come from these men. "Far more than a majority . . . reported that their discoveries came in moments of relaxation following upon weeks of intensive application. The solution . . . did not arrive as the result of cold logical reasoning, but arrived in consciousness full and complete at off moments and under varying circumstances."

And Williams tells the story of Dr. F. G. Banting. One night, Banting was preparing to lecture on diabetes to his medical students. The information on diabetes was mixed, confusing, useless. Banting worked late, and went to bed. He awoke at two o'clock in the morning, with a research idea, which he at once wrote down: "Tie off the pancreatic duct of dog. Wait six to eight weeks for degeneration. Re-

† John K. Williams, *The Wisdom of Your Subconscious Mind* (Englewood Cliffs, N.J.: Prentice-Hall, 1964).

move residue and extract." He did this, he gave the world insulin, and diabetes came under control for millions.

A famous instance of insight included in Williams' book is that of Otto Loewi, pharmacologist, University of Graz. He awoke one night with an idea, made notes, and went back to sleep. The next day was a nightmare. He knew he had the idea, and he had the notes. But he could not read the notes. Amidst his familiar apparatus in his laboratory, he tried and tried to recall the idea. No success.

During the next night, he awoke with the same inspiration. This time he made *good* notes. The next day in his laboratory, ". . . in one of the simplest and most definite experiments in the history of biology, [he] brought proof of the chemical mediation of nerve impulses. This was the beginning of a host of investigations in many countries. . . ."

C. Guy Suits was placed in charge of all research at General Electric at age forty. He is quoted by Alex Osborn in *Your Creative Power*:‡

SUITS: [The *positive attitude*] is a characteristic of creative people. Form the habit of reacting *Yes* to a new idea. First, think of all the reasons why it's good; there will be plenty of people around to tell you why it won't work. . . . Be on the alert for hunches, and whenever you find one hovering on the threshold of your consciousness, welcome it with open arms. Doing these things won't transform you into a genius overnight. But they're guaranteed to help you locate that treasure chest of ideas which lie hidden at the back of your own brain. . . . It's generally a hunch that starts the inventor on his quest. . . . Later on, perhaps after weeks of fruitless searching, another inspiration, arriving when he least expects it, drops the answer in his lap. I've seen this happen over and over. But I've yet to meet that "coldly calculating man of science" whom the novelists extol. Candidly, I doubt that he exists; and if he did exist,

‡ Alex Osborn, *Your Creative Power* (New York: Charles Scribner's Sons, 1948).

I fear that he would never make a startling discovery or invention.

Let me call on a friend of many years, Dr. H. R. Crane, head of the Department of Physics at our university. Every physicist in the world knows his name. He was recently called to Toronto (where Banting worked) to be given the Davisson-Germer Prize, named for my instructor, Davisson, and his co-worker Germer—whose electron diffraction work proved that electrons can act like waves. The prize is given every other year for the best research concerning the electron, and is sponsored by Bell Telephone Laboratories. Crane's contribution was a unique and direct method for measuring the ratio of the free electron's magnetic moment to its spin angular momentum, known as the "g factor" of the electron.*

In 1959, Crane spoke at the National Science Fair in Flint, Michigan, on "Creative Thinking and Experimenting." In his speech, he deals at some length with Henri Poincaré, who made his own speech perhaps sixty years ago, in Paris, on his creative experiences. Crane describes Poincaré's method, as he experiences it:

CRANE: The way is to sit down and, consciously and with a good deal of self-discipline, force yourself to think hard about the problem. It usually takes, he finds, a number of hours, which may not necessarily be in a continuous stretch. The mental effort here must be great. But after the mental effort has been put forth, the problem thereafter haunts the mind; that is, you know your brain is working on it because bits of it keep entering the consciousness, at odd moments. Thereafter the subconscious work requires some time—perhaps days or even months. A booster shot of conscious effort may be required from time to time, but in the main you can do other things with your conscious attention. Just when the solution will come (if at all) is entirely unpredictable.

* H. R. Crane, "The g Factor of the Electron" (*Scientific American,* January 1968).

SUMMARIZING

It is time to try to summarize what these highly creative men have tried to say to us. It would go something like this:

First, the problem is recognized. It may arise from a chance observation; it may be the challenge of an old puzzler that has stumped everyone; it may be the need for a new material, handed to a lab research team; or any other circumstance that poses a challenge.

Second, there is a deep involvement, a strong desire to solve the problem.

Third, a good deal of conscious effort is put forth, of whatever kind is necessary. It may require reading the literature. It may require apparatus, experimentation, the gathering of data, or it may not; it invariably calls for a lot of hard thinking.

Fourth, straightforward reasoning cannot be expected to solve the problem. If that were true, many workers in an active field would be able to do that reasoning, and no really creative end-product would come out: It would just be an answer to a problem that many could solve. And that answer would come in the conscious-work period.

Fifth, intuition, or hunch, must be openly entertained and welcomed. In fact, the whole operation often starts with a hunch.

Sixth, those who play this game know perfectly well that the ultimate insight, inspiration, or "flash of genius" is not expected to come during conscious work and hard thinking. They do solidly rely on its coming at some totally unpredictable moment, when not engaged in the conscious work, and usually when away from where that work is done.

Not any of those in this, and the preceding chapter, were psychologists. They have had to choose their own expressions, and describe their creative experiences as best they could. Suppose we could ask those who used the word "subconscious," "What do you mean by that, and how does it operate for you?" They would be hard put to give an answer that would satisfy. Psychologists have not found it an easy question to answer.

More and more, the psychology of creativity is being intensively studied. Progress is being made. More and more, creative people are learning enough of the psychology of creativity, the better to direct their own efforts and to be more successful. Later in this book, we must turn to the subconscious, and hopefully, see more clearly the indispensable role it plays in this fascinating game of bringing something new into existence.

SIX

So You, Too, Have an Idea?

Right here, approaching the middle of the book, why not swing squarely around to *you*? You have ideas. Aren't there some things you can do about them, even before you know enough about creativity to give lectures on it? There surely are. What about proper objectives? What about testing an idea? What about how one thing can lead to another? What about judgment? Prejudgment? All such matters, and many others, came into the lives of earlier discoverers and inventors, long before anyone was writing papers and books about creativity and the creative process. So, you too, have an idea? How well are you *already* prepared to do at least something about it?

WHAT YOU ALREADY KNOW

You are, say, seventeen. Therefore, you have already learned a tremendous lot about this world of ours. Just in growing up, going places, interacting with people, seeing houses built, buying groceries for mom, eating, sleeping, getting sick and getting well again—all this and a great deal more has taught you much.

Along with this, you have read a lot, and that has opened your mind to a wide variety of places and things you have not yourself seen. So, without ever going to school, you would already have acquired a great deal of knowledge —far more than you are inclined to give yourself credit for. Add in the school experience, with the knowledge and skills learned there, and we have to insist that you are remarkably well equipped to entertain ideas in numerous directions.

A young fellow with creative urges wants to do some pioneering. Once upon a time, you could have gone West to help open up the country. Mostly, that time is past (although Alaska, Canada, and Australia still offer you plenty of room for that). Your pioneering yearnings may instead be in terms of wanting to go straight up, in space exploration. That's as new as today and tomorrow. But, much as that may appeal, don't forget the river where you like to canoe. Once a decent stream, it is now polluted. It needs your ideas and your support for turning it into a clean stream again; and the chances are that by the time you are ready to help out, the pollution will still be there, waiting for you. There's a million other things needing your creative pioneering.

And you have an idea? Fine! Where do you go from there?

YOUR IDEA—OLD OR NEW?

When you get a bright idea, your immediate attitude toward it could be at either of two extremes. The optimistic extreme: "This is *my* idea; nobody ever thought of it before; how fast can I get a patent on it, before somebody else thinks of it?" The pessimistic extreme: "Aw, shucks; I'm only seventeen. What chance do I have of thinking of something really new? This must have been invented a thousand times over!"

Which is the proper attitude? *Neither.*

Be an optimistic pessimist. Have the good sense to realize that especially in older, well-developed areas, many ingenious people have been busy, long before you came along; and in such areas, the idea is very probably old. (Even so, you are still entitled to the thrill of having *independently* created it.) But, on the opposite side, keep hope alive. Occasionally there is a case where everyone else has missed the boat.

My favorite illustration is so much to the point that I always include it in my lectures on creativity. These often are at universities, with faculty members present (and this gives me a good chance to rub it in). I remind them that nearly all of my listeners either play pool, or are very familiar with the game from watching it. Next, I tell them that nearly all are thoroughly familiar with a property of the ellipse: that a line from one of the two foci, reflected from the elliptical boundary at equal angles, would go to the other focus. Then: Here are all of the elements needed for inventing a new pool table and pool game. How? We put a spot to mark one focus, on an elliptical pool table. At the other focus, we put a pocket. If the cue ball drives a ball across the spot, the cushion will "reflect" it to the pocket. In a different shot, you make a ball leave the pocket, on a line through the pocket; it is reflected to cross the spot, and then go on by a second reflection, to the pocket.

Millions of Americans, young and old, have had a full chance to make this invention. They didn't. And then?

A student, Arthur P. Frigo, built the first elliptical pool table, and installed it in his fraternity house at Union College in 1962. No doubt, study habits went to pieces for a while. In April of that year, Frigo obtained his patent: No. 3,029,078. And when did he get this concept? When working on a high school math project. Take a look at it in Plate 10.

What if young Frigo had said, "Aw, shucks—millions have had a chance to think of this"—and then gone on to other things?

I managed to locate Frigo and correspond with him. It is a rare pleasure to be able to give you the sequel. The game is on the market. His royalties have already repaid his college expenses, and paid for a new car; and the royalties are still coming in.

I don't play pool. But I have played three-cushion billiards for half a century, and have watched pool countless times. I know all about that property of the ellipse. I like to invent. I just wanted you to know that I am among all those who missed the boat, and left it to a student at Union College to make us all a little red around the ears.

WRONG OR IMPOSSIBLE OBJECTIVES

Every creative individual has his share of ideas or hunches that lead into dead-end streets: They turn out to be wrong, or even impossible of achievement. For example: In the long history of science, the Law of the Conservation of Energy has been with us, relatively, only a short time. This makes it easier to understand why so many good men used to try to invent perpetual motion. (Don't miss reading what Stanley W. Angrist has to say about this.*) Enticing as it may be to think of getting something for nothing, we know now that it can't be done. *Impossible objective* is the verdict.

Somewhere today, an uninformed inventor may have a big idea: Why not invent *super salt?* Ordinary salt is just so salty, and no more so. Why not make an *improved* salt (by appropriate chemistry) so that super salt is a hundred times saltier than the old-fashioned kind? You already know the answer. NaCl is just that; no more, no less; and it is going to stay that way. Nature has a stubborn insistence on refusing to let us violate her laws.

The sooner you find, somehow, that your attractive idea is an impossibility, the better; for then, you can turn to ideas with rosier prospects.

As to *wrong* objectives, we must proceed with care. An idea might be quite attainable in fact, but in a practical sense, be out of the question. It is then a wrong idea. For example, chocolate bars come wrapped. So do bars of soap. You know that automatic wrapping machinery does the wrapping. So you get this idea: Suggest to a chocolate company that since they already have that machinery, why not add soap manufacture, and use the machinery to wrap both products? Moreover, you could argue, correctly, that plant facilities for making both products are somewhat alike (both call for cooking, stirring, use of molds). And we know that companies *do* sometimes expand their lines of

* "Perpetual Motion Machines" (*Scientific American,* January 1968), pp. 114–22.

manufacture when they find that new items can be turned out on existing machinery.

So what's wrong? This: A chocolate company takes pride in the taste of its products, and spends plenty of advertising money to maintain the regard people have for its chocolate bars. Could you persuade that company to add its name to *soap*—a product the taste of which is such that you hope never to taste it again? The practical matter here is one of human reactions. I would judge this to be a wrong idea (but then, I might be wrong about that myself!).

A common example of a wrong idea is when it does have a principle working for it, but the principle is utterly inadequate. Here is an instance. A graduate student in architecture saw some pictures somewhere, and learned that electric fields have very lovely conformations. He also learned that electrostatic forces can be put to work, as in electrostatic spray painting. He somehow found that I know a little about these matters, and he brought his idea to me. Roughly, it was to get new decorative effects by making electrostatics do two things at once. He would apply plaster or cement coatings onto walls electrostatically, and at the same time make the applied material form into those lovely curves as dictated by the electric field. Give him all credit for imagination. But what's wrong? Electrostatic forces *can* move tiny paint particles, but never can they be used to throw heavy plaster mixes around.

You are under pressure to create an entry for a science fair. You happen to think of two masses, and how they attract each other. You also know the law: The force is proportional to the product of the masses, divided by the square of the distance between their centers of mass. Aha! Why not work this up into a beautiful demonstration? Hang one mass on a long wire; arrange to make the other one move closer to it, and demonstrate that the first one swings slightly toward it. What's wrong with that? Nothing, in theory. The trouble is that the effect working for you is so extremely weak that *other* effects (vibration, air movement, distortion of the building as people walk around, etc.) would completely smother the effect you want to demonstrate—unless you go to massive, refined equipment. (But again, you might take my statement as a challenge, become creative, and come up with a new set of ideas for this demonstration that would be widely acclaimed.)

There is another reason for treating this "wrong idea" with care. Time and again, the "experts" have declared an idea to be wrong, when it was right and they were wrong. Never forget Clarence Darrow, and his million-dollar game of "Monopoly." A classic case arose when Edison declared that an electric generator should have *as low an internal resistance as feasible*. He was declared wrong by the experts, here and abroad. Some even attacked him as dishonest. But Edison went right ahead and built his generators that way. Edison was right, and so were his generators.

TESTING AN IDEA

There is now a great flurry of interest in developing a car to be powered by storage batteries, or fuel cells. You know one reason, of course: The gasoline engine contributes to the air pollution menace in several ways. You get to thinking about all this, and an idea is born. You remember that slingshot you had, powered by rubber bands. You once had a toy airplane, likewise powered. Well: Why not drive a car with stretched rubber bands? Your next move *could* be to hunt up a mechanical engineer, and get his judgment on the idea.

Instead, let's see how far you could go, entirely on your own, to test the idea. Could large rubber bands be made? Of course. Could you drive such a car up to a service station and get a "refill"? No. Not now. But this has to be a *big* idea. You are thinking of millions of these cars, with stations adapted to serve them. There, you would connect to a motor-driven source, and get your bands stretched tight again in a few minutes. No trouble at all so far, and nothing but thinking required, so far. One more "thinking" test: Would that much rubber be too costly? You don't know, and you put that question aside for the time being. If further tests do not condemn the idea, you can look into that; if they do, there won't be any need to worry about cost.

PLATE I   Benjamin Franklin, one of the "greats" of all time.
(Photograph from Burndy Library)

PLATE 2 Michael Faraday, the ablest experimenter the world has known. *(Photograph from Burndy Library)*

PLATE 3 Thomas Alva Edison, the greatest inventor. (*Photograph by permission of U.S. Department of the Interior, National Park Service, Edison National Historic Site*)

PLATE 4   Alexander Graham Bell, with blind and deaf boy. (*Photograph by Gilbert H. Grosvenor © National Geographic Society*)

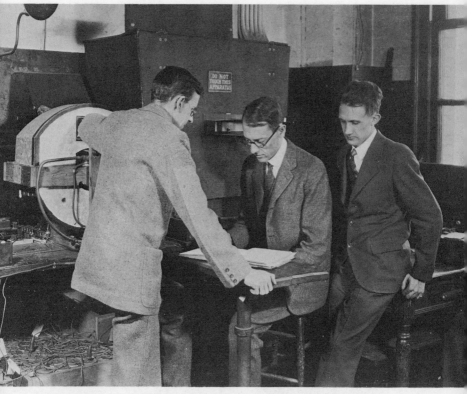

PLATE 5   C. J. Davisson, with Germer and an aide in his laboratory. Davisson shared a Nobel Prize with Sir George Thomson for discovering that electrons can behave like waves. (*Photograph from Burndy Library*)

PLATE 6   John R. Pierce. His many contributions include playing an important role in developing Project Echo, the forerunner
of Telstar. (*Photograph from Bell Telephone Laboratories*)

PLATE 7 H. R. Crane. For devising a way to measure the "g factor" of the electron, he received the Davisson-Germer prize. (*University of Michigan News Service*)

PLATE 8   The Transistor Group. By bringing the transistor into
existence, they revolutionized much of electronics. William Shock-
ley, seated; John Bardeen, standing left; and Walter Brattain.
(*Photograph from Bell Telephone Laboratories*)

Next, you might think of becoming a young design engineer, starting at the library: Go there and look up rubber, and find how much energy can be stored in it. Now, it is true that immense amounts of data are in print, waiting for you, in all sorts of fields. A vast number of the more ordinary, often-needed facts is on record. But often, you find that the very piece of information you need can't be found. You might not find rubber's ability to store energy.

Instead of "looking it up," you think of another attack: turn yourself into a young experimental engineer. Get some rubber bands, and do some testing. So you get a bundle of bands, all alike, and test one. You find how much weight you have to hang onto it to stretch it, say, to five times the relaxed length. You test several others, to get an average value. Then you pile enough bands on the postal scales to get a pretty good measure of their weight. You count them. You now figure the energy in foot-pounds you can store in that weight of rubber.

Now for the car. How much of its total weight can be in rubber? You don't know, so you guess, half. Next, what about friction loss in the whole system, and power needed to drive it through the air? Here, you are stumped. Without that, how can you find how far your car could go on the level, on one stretching? But you don't give up. You recall that a car has to climb hills. In going up a 5 per cent grade, it will take a known number of foot-pounds to lift the car five feet, in going one hundred feet. Just to see how it works out, give yourself a break at this point, assume there are no losses, and that all of the stored energy goes to lift the car. When you find how far up the grade the car would go, you won't need to test the idea any further. You grin, and file the idea in the wastebasket.

HOW ONE THING CAN LEAD TO ANOTHER

Time and again, when an inventor or a research team works toward one objective, something totally unexpected happens that opens up a new line of investigation. Sometimes, the unexpected feature becomes far more important than the original quest. In the case below, the side issue has no real importance; but it does satisfy curiosity, and it adds to judgment—and these *are* important.

We have concentrated on running a car with rubber bands. The unexpected idea is this: How high could a rubber band lift itself? We think of rigging a vertical pipe and evacuating it to cut out air resistance. At the lower end would be a stretched band, to be released and shoot itself up the pipe. How high would it go?

Now, here is a case where you and I have had *some* experience. We have all shot our share of bands across the room, when there is air resistance. Our judgment is good, for these conditions. If we step outdoors, we could make a fair guess at how high we could shoot the band. But until we try it (or figure it) for a vacuum, our judgment could be way off for guessing the in-vacuum height. Get ready for a surprise. The measurements and figures for my rubber band say that, ignoring internal losses, it would rise to 270 feet! All of which expands judgment—that precious factor that tells us how to do things right, or often says to us, "Check it—there's a mistake!"

In Chapter Ten, you will read how Irving Langmuir set out to solve one problem, met with a surprise, went to work on that, and came up with a result of great economic importance. One thing can lead to another!

RELAXING YOUR REQUIREMENTS

Perfection is unattainable. If your creative idea calls for a perfect material, give up: There is none. But there are many fine materials, some of which may serve your need in excellent style. If you want a perfect nonconductor of heat, you can't have it; but there are ways to cut heat loss to reasonable levels, in a great variety of cases. If you want 100 per cent efficiency in a battery, you will never get it; but do you *really* need it? Time and again, a requirement we *think* we must meet, as to a material, or process, or function, is really "just an idea." When the requirement is relaxed, we steam ahead.

In engineering, there are no perfect solutions. What we really are after are the best compromises. In science, there is no perfect apparatus; what is needed is apparatus that is good enough for the purpose.

The fluid mappers I have developed nicely illustrate what we discuss here. You can see one in Plate 14, as it appeared on the cover of *Scientific American* for July 1967.† A fluid mapper operates immersed in a fluid, usually water (water is cheap!). There is an upper member, plate glass, through which we look or photograph. Below it is the lower member, which I call the slab. There is a *thin* flow space between the two. By means of a mouth or well or a hole or holes in the slab, connected to a tank or tanks, flow is induced in the thin flow space. Dye lines from potassium permanganate crystals make the flow pattern visible. The pattern then represents the lines of some *potential field*, such as a magnetic or electric field, or a heat conduction field. You see those lines in Plate 14. Also, the water supplied by the central well has been colored differently from that supplied equally by the six outer wells. Innumerable field problems arise, calling for solution. Thus, slabs of almost any shape may be needed. Therefore, the slab material must be something that is easily worked up and modified.

When I began developing fluid mappers some twenty years ago, it was easy for me to lay down three requirements for the slab material. It must be tough and strong and rigid, and resist breakage. It must be insoluble in water. It must be impermeable, allowing no water leakage through itself.

Common sense dictated the first two requirements. Theory called for the third. And then? *No progress was made until I violated all three of my own requirements.* I adopted *plaster.* There are many plasters—plaster of Paris, wall plaster, and so on. What I use is what the dentists call dental stone (ask your dentist!). If I drop a slab, it breaks (but I have made perhaps two thousand slabs, and dropped but one). Plaster is slightly soluble in water; prolonged immersion lets it lose surface material, leading to error (but

† In that issue, simpler fluid mappers are described in the Amateur Scientist section, edited by C. L. Stong.

the usual use is so brief, it doesn't matter). Plaster has porosity: Water does soak through it, and there is leakage that theory would frown on (but it is so small that it doesn't matter either).

In return for not just relaxing, but *violating* my own three eminently "reasonable" requirements, I was able to go ahead—for plaster is cheap, and wonderfully workable and adaptable in several very important ways.

There is more to this story. Back around 1900, Professor Hele-Shaw, at Oxford, England, was the first to give the world such devices. He used plate glass for the upper member *and* for the lower member. He did some superb work; highly accurate work, too. These fluid flow simulations of fields were much needed for solving vexing field problems. His work was enthusiastically welcomed. But he hung onto that lower member of plate glass (strong, insoluble, leakproof), and his admirable contribution laid right down and died, until I had the privilege of moving ahead with it, half a century later. I admit to taking some pride in the fact that, as these particular lines are written, I am in my laboratory, which is unofficial world headquarters for fluid mapper activity.

Why did Hele-Shaw's work die? When a new field problem comes along, demanding some crazy boundary shape for the slab, and perhaps an equally dizzy shape of a well—just how do you easily and cheaply modify plate glass?

HOW MANY REQUIREMENTS
CAN YOU SPECIFY FOR A MATERIAL?

You have an idea for a physical device. It must be built of materials. Well, we have an enormous number of materials. A Du Pont advertisement for nylon tells me that in the twenty-five years after 1919, using carbon, hydrogen, oxygen, and nitrogen, more than two hundred thousand compounds wholly new to man came along. Since then, still more; and vast numbers of other compounds have emerged. But suppose one critically important part of your device must meet certain requirements:

Requirement 1. It must be rigid and quite strong. Available: thousands of metallic alloys; dozens of plastics; numerous types of glass and ceramics; many kinds of rocks.

Requirement 2. It must conduct electricity. Available: thousands of metallic alloys.

Requirement 3. It must be very easily machined. Available: dozens of metallic alloys.

Requirement 4. Cost per pound must be low. Available: a few.

Requirement 5. It must be available in many sizes in rod and sheet form. Available: aluminum and brass.

Requirement 6. It must be easily soldered. Available: brass.

Requirement 7. After being polished, it must not tarnish in the open air.

Available: NONE!

Sometimes, only one or two requirements will bring us to "none available." Whereupon we give up. Or do we? Hopefully, we find a way to relax some requirements, find a suitable material, and go ahead.

Let us pause here, to let this little study bring out a point of the greatest importance. Any number of times, discoverers and inventors have come up against "none available." Whereupon, creativity was turned loose to *make* the needed material available. And then, often enough, not only was the immediate need fulfilled, but a market has unfolded to put the new material to work in all sorts of other ways. Thus does frustration lead to success.

Bringing new materials into existence is now one of the most active areas of technology. *Scientific American,* with a readership of four hundred thousand, devoted the issue for September 1967 to what? Materials!

THE BICYCLE PROBLEM

I ride an English-made Raleigh bicycle, winter and summer. Do I believe that the bicycle has reached the ultimate in development? Emphatically not! Neither does a British

engineer, D. G. Wilson, now at M.I.T. As I write, he is
offering a prize of five hundred pounds for design improvements in man-powered transport. "At present, the bicycle
provides most such transportation. In most developing
countries the bicycle is virtually the sole means of medium-
and long-distance transport available to a large proportion
of the population, but development has been almost at a
standstill during this century. Some of the troubles with
the bicycle are that it requires too much effort to propel it,
it deposits dirt on the rider, the rim brake drastically loses
efficiency in wet weather, repairs and maintenance take an
inordinate amount of time and skill, in a collision or spill
there is a high probability of injury to the rider, and pound
for pound it costs about three times as much as a typical
light car."‡ All of these things are true.

Take the chain, for example. If you keep it greased or
oiled, it collects dirt and grit. If you don't, it rusts. My chain
is always rust-threatened in winter, when salt is used on
icy streets. Perhaps you have thought of a transmission shaft,
with gears at each end, and sealed against entry of dirt and
water. Undoubtedly, it has been tried; but I suspect that it
is a high-cost idea. Right now, fluid drives are being very
rapidly adapted for mechanical-drive applications. I don't
know enough about them to discuss this possibility for a
bike; but I know enough about bikes to wish ardently for a
really good transmission. Maybe one of you will invent it,
and thus make the first major improvement since Musselman invented the coaster brake.

THE DIPSTICK PROBLEM

How do I know when my car needs oil? The man at the
gas station raises the hood, removes and wipes the dipstick,
shoves the stick down, pulls it out again, sees where the oil
clings to it, and says, "You are down a quart." In doing that,
he uses a very simple, very cheap device that never wears
out, and that *can* have complete reliability. But it takes time.
These days, we tend to have information come to us *auto-*

‡ (*Engineering Education*, November 1967).

matically. When I drive to a gas station, I do not need to ask if the car needs gasoline. The instrument on the dash has already told me that. Why isn't there another instrument that tells me how much oil to buy? For after all, running out of gas merely means getting stalled. To run out of oil is to buy a new engine. Talk with a man who knows engines, and he will tell you how a lot of the oil in a running engine is up in the parts, doing its job; and that no one knows how to devise an instrument that says, on the road, how much oil is needed. Also, he will say that *after* stopping, there should be a waiting period before using the dipstick, to let most of that in-use oil run down to the pool. Well then, *after* stopping, why not have an instrument that indicates oil level? Could you invent one?

On the pessimistic side, you have two strikes against you. First, if your gadget costs a dollar or more, you will join the hundreds of others who also want to "improve" the auto for only a dollar or more in one way or another. Second, reliability: Could you guarantee that your device is going to be utterly and always and completely reliable? You could not. Would you run a chance and trust *your* engine with a device that nearly always told the truth—but not always? So, without looking into the several (or perhaps many) ways this could be done, you know that nearly all—and perhaps all—possible ways will have to be rejected for occasional unreliability.

So much for pessimism. But there is more to be said. Is the cheap, simple, foolproof dipstick invariably reliable? *It* is; but *people* may not be. A careless attendant may not put the stick clear down. A crooked attendant *will not* put it clear down—he wants to sell oil; or he quickly uses the stick before the oil draindown has happened. And now, here's an actual experience of the opposite kind. After my Canadian interlude, when most of this book was written, we loaded our station wagon, drove into Blind River, and got ready to drive the 440 miles home. I got gas. A young attendant checked the oil. Verdict: "Full up." I had a different feeling about it. Instead of dealing with him further, I stopped at the next station for an oil check. The man was able to get only a drop clinging to the bottom of the stick!

The dipstick is a reliable device. Not all users of it are reliable.

I recently talked with some automotive engineers about this problem. As you should expect, it is a problem that the industry has fussed and worried over for decades. They are still fussing and worrying about it. Meantime, all cars have dipsticks! Can you think of something new in this area?

A VERY HIGH OBSERVATORY

Of course, you are interested in astronomy. Who isn't? And you know that good observatories are put up on mountains, at high extra cost. They have to be up where the air is clear. Even so, there is a lot of atmosphere above them, and it plays nasty tricks on the astronomer. Irregular air temperatures make the star images waver about. Another thing: The atmosphere heavily absorbs ultraviolet; until we began to put instruments into orbit, we knew little about that end of the sun's spectrum, and even less about stars with energy outputs mainly in the ultraviolet. Today, vast sums are spent on rockets and satellites, some of it for the benefit of astronomy. Therefore, an idea everyone would have discarded twenty years ago because of great cost might today get some attention.

An idea I have had lately—and I can't get it off my mind —is to build a very high observatory. As far as I can find out, it has never been proposed. Why not invite you to have some creative fun thinking about it? If you go up 3.4 miles, half the atmosphere is below you. Another equal distance, and three-quarters is below you; another, and seven-eighths is left below. Up that high, the cloud problem would seldom bother, even in a cloudy area; and many observations could be made to far better effect. If we can build Eiffel Towers and hundred-story buildings, why can't we pick out a mountain two miles high, plant a seven-mile-high observatory on it, and get our instruments nine miles up in the air? Now, noncreative people seem to like to prejudge an idea adversely. One such could easily point out that astronomers do not work in space suits. True; but we come right back at him. Good astronomers will do almost anything to add to our knowledge. Then the killjoy might say that the erectors of the structure would also have to wear space suits. Surely—and so what? We already know that this won't be easy.

Is this a crazy idea? How could you test it right now, long before taking a couple of degrees and then getting a lot of experience in structural design? One of the great values of having creative ideas when young comes in the very testing of them. An idea might be wacky; but in looking into it, interesting problems arise, new channels of thought are opened up, new knowledge is gained, judgment is enhanced. You learn to chop out all details, and reduce the main problem to its simplest possible form.

Get your thinking started on this problem by asking how high a solid steel cylinder could be. That would be as high as would bring it to the allowable compression stress at the base. I'll let you use two hundred thousand pounds per square inch for that, and about 0.28 pound per cubic inch for steel. You figure it out. How high?

You do some more thinking: This thing will need an adequate base to give it rigidity, and to anchor it firmly to the rock. You mentally picture the Eiffel Tower, and how it is tapered. We had better taper our tower, too. Make it horn-shaped. But if made solid, it would call for impossibly large amounts of steel. But don't make it solid. Make it like a horn, a curved, tapered tube. But: How to taper it? Go ahead and *taper* it, your own way, and see how it comes out. For example, you make the base two miles in diameter. You decide to shrink the diameter by a factor, the square root of 0.5, or 0.707, for each mile up. The radii, in miles, would be a series: 1, 0.707, 0.5, 0.3535, etc. to a top diameter of 0.088 mile, or 930 feet. Then you draw the profile and look at it, long and hard. Does it look rigid enough? (My drawing makes it look at least hopeful, to me.) Next, that wide top: We want an observatory up there, not a football field. But we can reduce that to, say, one hundred feet, or fifty, by a more rapid shrinking as we near the top.

Having rigidity in mind, and conserving on steel, you

reach a further decision: Not only taper off on diameter, but also taper off on wall thickness. Perhaps you try making the wall two feet thick at the bottom, and taper off to one inch thick at the top, in a regular way. That puts you in a position to do some critical and informative figuring. What is your compression stress at the bottom? And at several levels as you go up? These may require a new start. Or if not, then go ahead and take the big step: Figure the tons of steel needed, and then find out how many tons the world produces in a year. Of course, it will call for a fantastic amount of steel, and a fantastic cost to build the tube. But after all, big things start with big dreams. If we could build such a tower with international cooperation, over a forty-year period, it might get consideration. Don't forget that all the way up, the meteorological people would have it adorned with instruments to get data they very much need. So would workers concerned with air pollution, fallout, and so on. It would be very much of a multipurpose tower.

The actual design would call for a vast amount of pioneer engineering. Should it be a closed tube? Or should it be an open-structure affair? All sorts of new and interesting studies and decisions would have to be made. This would indeed be quite a project! I have my own guess as to whether it is barely within the realm of possibility; or just a dream completely beyond realization. I'll let you play with it, free from any prejudgment I might give it.

JUDGMENT

That precious element we call *judgment* enables us to draw on experience, size up a situation, and say, "Make this part bigger," or "I'm sure it will work," or "It is going to clear up—let's hold the picnic." Basically, there is no substitute for actual experience in forming good judgments of many kinds. You and I know, from experience, about what to expect as to distance and accuracy when we shoot a rubber band across a room: We've *done* it. On the other hand, we have never shot a band upward in a vacuum. But if we have figured out how far it would go, we have had some imagined experience, and have thereby extended our judgment. An experienced design engineer has excellent judgment; an indispensable part comes from intimately knowing his machines at firsthand, and the rest of it from calculating the strength of parts, predicting performance, and that sort of thing.

You are already splendidly equipped with judgment derived from leading an active life. Here comes a tennis ball, low and fast. Shall you plop it just over the net, or smash it fast into the backstretch? In this and in all other active sports, your judgment gets honed to a pretty fine edge. Your kid brother's kite is up there on the end of a limb and he wants you to get it. Will the limb hold you? Having had a lot of "limb experience," your judgment says, go ahead, but with care.

Do creative scientists and engineers need good judgment? They surely do. A lot of it comes from actually working with apparatus, machines, experiments, and so on; and a lot more comes from the imagined experience acquired by designing the apparatus, predicting its performance, taking data, and turning it into the answers sought.

A brilliant man with poor judgment can actually be a hazard. On the other hand, many a valuable contribution has come from men of ordinary intelligence but with excellent judgment.

PREJUDGMENT

It occurs to you to power a car by stretched rubber bands. If next you said to yourself, "This is silly," or "Many must have thought of that, and found it won't work," or "It will call for just too much mechanical gear for speed and torque control," then you would have prejudged your idea. You could prejudge the attraction between two masses by guessing that the force would be far too small. But that would deprive you of the value of going ahead to find how small it is, and how tiny the deflection would be.

When searching for ideas or entertaining them, a habit of prejudging can have an inhibiting effect.

Those who advocate "brainstorming" lay great stress on this. They say that in that phase of creating when ideas are badly needed, the mind should be allowed to run wild, and come up with notions, many of which may be foolish. To stop and prejudge each idea as it occurs, they say, can be deadly. There is much truth in this.

The most insistent "prejudger" I ever met was a former student. He must have descended from a long line of perfected pessimists. He was the class nuisance. Whenever I would start to describe some new development that deserved our attention, his hand would shoot up, and he would think of something to say against it. When he exhausted my patience, I laid a trap for him. I went to class and opened right up with this question: What do you think of making a flashlight without cells? Just put a little electric generator inside, and a handle to squeeze in the hand? Give it a flywheel, put a spring return on the squeezer, keep pumping, and always have some light handy? At once, his hand shot up. He took the bait. He raised some objection. Then I pulled exactly that flashlight out of my pocket and operated it. (I am told that many were used in World War II.) Did it cure him? No. Nothing would.

SEVEN

Learning, Observing, Visualizing

As a highly creative young person with broad interests, you look ahead to a creative career. In this, you face two unpredictables. First, you cannot be sure of the paths along which your motivations, interests, and work may lead you. Second, you cannot predict all you will need to know or be aware of in that dimly perceived future. Here is a challenge and a problem. To put it in the extreme, should you try to learn everything about everything; or should you say, "When I need to know something, I'll look it up"?

LEARNING

When you create something new, everything in it comes out of that brainbox of yours. And if you *could* perform the creative act, except that just one essential item is not in your posssessed knowledge, you are not going to be successful. That which isn't in your head can't come out. Many an inventor has toiled and sweated to produce an invention that would not come through. Then, somewhere, he sees or reads of a mechanism or material or process he had not known about, and instantly recognizes that his troubles are over.

"Learn to think; don't memorize; you can look it up when you need it." Ever hear that? Millions of us have been told that. That statement can be as true as can be, and as false as can be. If it means, don't memorize the log table, it is true. If it means, consistently refuse to memorize nearly everything, it is deadly advice. When you talk with successful scientists and engineers, you are always talking to men who have learned (memorized) a huge storehouse of information; but at the same time, these men freely resort to papers, books, handbooks, and tables for information not frequently needed, or too vast to be memorized. (Don't get the wrong idea: they do not sit around for hours, painfully storing away facts and such; they learn the easy and best way—by being intensely interested in their work; and a great deal of learning occurs automatically.)

A young person with a creative career ahead can never start too soon to acquire a truly impressive inventory of facts, laws, principles, relationships, and properties. Heat flows from hot to cold objects. Masses attract each other. A current crossing a magnetic field has a crosswise force acting on its conductor. Acids and alkalis react to form neutral salts. Salts in solution separate into positive and negative ions. Water is most dense at 4 degrees Centigrade. In a lake the "spring overturn" comes when the ice melts, the cold water goes down, displaces the warmer water below, and brings it up. Gases expand when heated if free to do so; if not, the pressure goes up. The human eye is sensitive to a wavelength range from 0.4 to 0.7 micron. The sun emits in a very wide spectrum, with plenty of invisible infrared energy; in observing an eclipse with cheap colored glasses that will pass the infrared, the infrared may heat the retina and give you a blind spot for life. The air is about 21 per cent oxygen; the remainder, mostly nitrogen; but a tiny fraction of carbon dioxide (about four parts in ten thousand) has a tremendous influence on our climate. An *exceedingly* small amount of ozone, mostly higher up, is all that stands between us and death, by largely absorbing the sun's ultraviolet. Puncture wounds are dangerous, not only from the chance of ordinary infection: Organisms of lockjaw and gas gangrene cannot tolerate much oxygen, and, carried into the body, they may develop. The hyperbaric (high-pressure) chamber can save victims of these often fatal diseases by flooding the tissues with oxygen (by greatly increasing the amount dissolved in the blood plasma at the higher pressure). The young of small birds are hatched cold-blooded, typically taking nine days to reach full thermoregulation. Bears do not hibernate, in the true sense of the word. Some bat species hibernate daily: After feeding, the bat hangs up in a cave, goes to sleep, and body temperature soon drops to near the air temperature. Wherever we go, we are constantly exposed to radiation from cosmic ray effects, and from the earth's radioactive content.

There will always be some who ask, "Why acquire a huge store of unorganized knowledge?" The successfully creative man does not ask that question. First, a great deal of his knowledge *is* organized. Second, he knows from experience that if one certain "little" fact or law or effect must be had, and it is not in his memory store, and if he happens not to find it—he is stuck.

Suppose you are deeply interested in electromechanical devices, but are bored by optics. Anything you see about optics, you pass up. Then comes a day when an important device you are working up would come through, *if* you could just manage to do one thing in it, simply, reliably, and cheaply. Fiber optics would be just the thing. But while millions of others are aware of fiber optics, you barely know it exists, and a vital factor in your device may not occur to you at all. (Let's hope someone else makes the suggestion before it is too late.)

W. R. G. Baker has put it very well. He was Vice President, Electronics Department, General Electric Company, for years. He says the creative thinker ". . . must constantly enlarge his store of knowledge—through study and observation. This is extremely important since it represents the inventory of raw material out of which ideas are produced."*

So much for the steady, day-by-day acquiring of knowledge. But what about doing additional learning, when taking up a project creatively? Should we begin a research project by "reading up" on it? Sir J. J. Thomson, who discovered the electron, thought not. We learn this from his son, Sir George Thomson. "J.J." disagreed with what was usual: to read up on the literature when facing a new

---

* His article, "You Too Can Think Creatively," appeared in *IRE Student Quarterly*, September 1960.

problem. He held out for giving it independent thought leading to one's own independent approach. Read later, he said, about what has already been done; doing it too soon may stifle original ideas.

Now we had better make a distinction here. J. J. Thomson is saying that to read the older literature bearing on that area of research may stifle originality. But another kind of reading may be in order. This is when the project requires knowing about a subject that is new to us. Suppose there is a mechanical device to be perfected. It requires gears. We have all seen many ordinary gear trains in clocks, watches, and other things; but the ordinary gear trains just will not suit the need. Then somehow, for the first time, we learn about *planetary gears*. To us, they are new, fascinating, stimulating. They solve our problem. I am sure that Thomson would agree that this kind of "reading up" is not only essential, but highly beneficial to the creative process.

AN EXCURSION INTO THE SUBJECT OF GLASS

I will now make up a little story about "Jones." Jones graduated in engineering with honors a year ago, was promptly hired, and displayed ability. He joined a small firm, hoping soon to be given responsibility. He was. The busy boss handed him a project and a budget and told him to go ahead. He did. Got some things done, too. But when the boss got back from an extended trip, he found the project hung up. Why? Well, as the boss knew, the apparatus called for a flat surface, a foot square. No, not perfectly flat; a near-optical flat. Jones had placed the order with an outside firm. He stated the price (very high); and delivery time (yet another month). That's when the boss went through the ceiling. Mentally, of course. Actually, he took a deep breath, controlled himself, and remarked that he could drive downtown and have the desired flat back within an hour by spending a dollar or so on a piece of plate glass. And now I will say why I made up that little story.

In lecturing at colleges and universities, I am often asked to take over a class to talk about creativity. I take along a piece of glass, about four inches square. I show it around. Perhaps one senior in ten can positively identify it for what it is: plate glass. Very few can tell me the difference between window glass and plate glass. Hardly anyone can say how plate glass is made, and why its price is high compared to window glass. Yet every engineering senior has seen any amount of both kinds; and glass, in general, is a tremendously important material in many areas of science and engineering.

The sad fact is that in this age of science, we keep our students in high school and college so busy learning theory, that unless the creative student strikes out on his own to get a broad background knowledge of machines, materials, processes, and so on, he may be a Jones, hanging up a project and spending a big wad of money totally needlessly. Do I exaggerate? I certainly do not. What can you do for yourself? Plenty. Look through catalogs of scientific supply houses. Look through *any* catalog. Read the advertisements in technical and scientific journals, to see who makes what. Never miss a chance to go through any laboratory, any factory, any machine shop. If you get to know a mechanic, toolmaker, die sinker, welder, or glassblower, make friends with him and pump him dry.

Back to plate glass. How is it made? A plate of somewhat uneven glass is imbedded in plaster, to make it stay fixed and unbending while being ground flat and polished by huge, flat grinding and polishing wheels. Then, with one side finished, it is broken loose, turned over, imbedded again, and the other side is finished. That costs money. The famed Pilkington firm in England thought it could be done better. They developed huge machines for grinding *both* sides at once. Faster. Also, the two sides come out parallel; the old way did not quite do that. But—could it be done even better? A member of the Pilkington family, while washing dishes at home one evening, saw the water running around, and things somehow clicked in his mind. And then, after spending millions in development, grinding and polishing were abolished. How? By continuously pouring a wide ribbon of molten glass onto a great long tank filled with molten tin. It comes off the other end, fire-polished on top, tin-polished below. How's that for ingenuity?

SERENDIPITY

Serendipity: an odd word that you often see in reading about creativity. It was coined by Hugh Walpole, as based on an ancient Ceylonese tale about Three Princes of Serendip. By accident or sharp observation, they were always discovering things not being looked for. Likewise for the creative scientist. He expects the unexpected to happen every so often. Instead of ignoring it, he comes wide awake and looks into it.

In a fine book‡ by Hans Selye, Selye warns about being so intent on what we are looking for and *intending* to observe, that the odd, the unusual, the exception, the "error," the misbehavior, may not even percolate into our consciousness. And it may be that this offbeat thing showing up (if we will only notice it) is much more important than the thing we seek at the time.

Selye also makes the point that the scientist needs erudition: to have read much and seen much. If he has a rich memory store, he has a much greater chance to connect the unexpected observation with what he already knows. Thus, recognizing its possible importance, he may go on to make a discovery.

Let me tell next about how serendipity worked for me, when some tiny little balls unexpectedly danced one day; and how, later, they floated when I didn't want them to.

OBSERVATION, CURIOSITY, DISCOVERY

One day in my laboratory, I wanted to investigate the magnetic field of a coil. It had no iron core. I wanted it to have one, right then. For other experiments, I had plenty of cast iron shot. (What is cast iron shot? If you melt cast iron and blow it into particles with steam, you make shot.) I

‡ *From Dream to Discovery* (New York: McGraw-Hill Book Company, 1964).

poured the coil full of shot, and turned on the alternating current. Some of the top shot proceeded to put on a dance! Being curious, I observed that dance. Somehow, some shot had become magnetized. Nothing told me at that moment, that much of my research time for the next three years would come out of that happening; and that two new lines of phenomena which I called electrospherics and magnetospherics* would be discovered and published and found fascinating by hundreds of engineers and scientists.

One thing these little magnetized balls do is run around in intricate fashion in a plastic bowl, when energized by a vertical alternating magnetic field. After I thought I had pretty well learned their tricks, I had one more idea: Would they do it under water? With water in the bowl, I poured in some shot, wanting them to sink. Instead, for the most part they floated. Refusing to be wetted, surface tension held them up. This was a nuisance. But I turned on the field anyway, and the nuisance turned into more discoveries! One of these is the "magic carpet," one of the most beautiful demonstrations I have ever seen. Imagine that you are looking down at a little inch-square pool of water. Floating on it is a single layer of balls, roughly 0.01 inch in diameter.

When the field is turned on, the balls go into action and completely organize themselves into a dynamic checkerboard formation of standing waves. A stop-action photo shows hills and hollows. A hill comes up to maximum, sinks down to become a hollow, and comes back up again, sixty times per second. A Strobotac (a lamp with adjustable flashing rate) is needed to slow down the action so that the eye can follow this fascinating performance. It is a dazzling show. No one has found any "use" for it yet, but that bothers me not at all.

Now, just one of the several effects that must combine to produce these ball-coated standing waves is concerned with this question: If a magnetized ball is floated on water in that magnetic field, what will it do? Will it align its

---

* A. D. Moore, "Electrospheric and Magnetospheric Phenomena" (Communications and Electronics, AIEE, November 1962).

magnetic axis with the field, or across it, or neither? A great number of men have worked on many aspects of magnetism, and the literature is enormous. Yet, as far as I know, no one could have told me the answer to that question. I am the discoverer, and I find that rewarding. The axis goes horizontal, the ball oscillates, and it sends out a train of waves each way from itself.

Several more things need be said about the "magic carpet." First, it was an accidental discovery, and in its first form was a moving, ever-changing raft of balls, free to roam on a larger water surface. Second, to make it happy, I then gave it a square (or rectangular) enclosure. Third, before writing a paper on it, I had to understand it, at least in fair degree. Fourth, my first ideas were completely wrong; not until the right hypotheses were entertained did the explanation unfold. Fifth, it depends on several rather delicately balanced effects. Sixth, I think it is millions to one that no one would ever have first thought of having such a thing as this "magic carpet," and then set out to produce it.

It is impossible to overestimate the importance of observation, curiosity, and accidental discovery. In his book, Beveridge (see Chapter Ten) does a splendid job of developing these subjects. He shows that time and again, keen observation of the unusual, the unexpected, can so often lead to something new; provided, of course, that curiosity is right there, to demand that it be followed up. And he makes much of the fact that so often, the intense curiosity of the child is succeeded by loss of curiosity in maturity. The creative person has curiosity in high degree. Beveridge gives many examples of how often a great advance is made through an accidental discovery. Of course, one can hardly plan a careerful of accidental discoveries. But experimenters are constantly exposed to errors, to the unusual, the unexpected. That little effect "that shouldn't be there" might make you famous!

In all of science, one of the most quoted statements is from Pasteur: "In the field of observation chance favors only the prepared mind."

Let me wrap up these thoughts in a "word equation": Observation + Curiosity + Investigation + Inspiration = Discovery.

OBSERVING A TYPEWRITER

Typing this manuscript brings back an observation I made at age nine. I then had borrowed a typewriter, along with a typing chart, and taught myself to finger correctly. That's when I discovered this curious fact: that the name of the device, *typewriter,* is spelled from the top row of letters only. As far as I know, this fact has never been published.

Now, those who have the best chance to observe this are women typists. Over the years, I have made it a point to ask many of them if they had made the observation. Not one ever had. Not one, that is, until very recently, when I found that Mrs. George Brockus, who had been a typist, did make the discovery. All credit to her!

Does all this say that women are not observant? Not on your life. But it may be a strong indicator of what we already know about men and women: Men can be very unobservant about some things; and women, about some other things. When it comes to matters that really interest them, women (I think) are more curious than men, and perhaps, are better observers.

THE SANDPIT AND SAND TRAIL MYSTERIES

Below our Canadian cabin is a sandy flat. Every summer for some years, it bothered me with two mysteries. I would find little conical pits here and there, perhaps half an inch deep. Also, in the mornings, I would find aimless little trails, as if tiny creatures had wandered around, each dragging a match, to leave a groove. I pondered these mysteries many times for some years and got nowhere. Soon after a return from Canada, I hopped to a convention in Texas. There was a barbecue under live oaks. There was a dusty road, and I walked along it. And right there in the dust, fifteen hundred miles from my two mysteries, the two became one, and the light dawned. For here was one pit, and from it ran a trail for some feet, and at the end of the trail, another pit! Ant lions!

Now, I had read about ant lions, and often thought about them. How can I excuse my miserable performance in having to go from border to border to get my answer? First, in reading about ant lions, they always seemed like something to be seen "somewhere else"—I wouldn't be lucky enough to meet them. Second, my reading had not mentioned trails (made when they change location). Third, it appears that they only trail at night. Fourth (if I may pile up my alibis), you never see an ant lion unless you dig him up; and even then, you'd never really notice him unless you expected him, and looked very closely. If you know about ant lions, fine. If not, you have some interesting reading to do.

IMAGINING, SENSING, VISUALIZING

The little child's imagination, unhampered by limited judgment, can mistake imagined things for reality. It can even go to where, if the child *thinks* he has done something, he believes it has been done. As we mature, the imagination gets channeled and tamed; and regrettably often, tamed down to where it is given only simple, needed tasks to perform. To go that route is to forego creativity. Creativity is a highly imaginative process.

The creative person calls every sense he has into play. Suppose we hand a chunk of a new plastic to a noncreative person. He notes the color (unavoidable). He hefts it, finding it light in weight (almost unavoidable). He squeezes it, and learns that it gives, but returns to shape again (he might have avoided that, so give him credit for the squeeze). Then he hands it back.

Then we give it to a creative person. He does all that the other fellow did, but more. He drops it to see if it bounces. He slices off a piece, finding it tough and resistant.

He sees that the color goes all the way through. He warms the slice in his hand, to see if it gets softer. He smells it. He probes us with questions. Name? Is it thermoplastic or thermosetting? Who makes it? Is it in production? What about cost? Will it stand up to weathering, and to the sun? And then, "May I have this sample?" Quite a difference, don't you think? The creative chap used his senses just as far as they would go, thus doing a fine *learning* job. And then, when the senses went as far as they could, he reached for more information through hearing—another sense. If you ever get to where you need to hire a highly creative man, casually hand the candidate some material he happens not to know, and watch the performance. It might save you from making a mistake.

Next, if we come back a year later and ask the creative fellow about that plastic, he will tell you all, or nearly all he learned about it, even if he has not touched it since. And while telling, he will be *visualizing* it. The appearance—color, shape, size—will occur to him as mental pictures. He will tell about its firmness when squeezed, and his imagination lets him live again the feel of it in his hand. If it had a faint odor, a bit like carbolic acid, perhaps —in imagination, he again smells it. Its density is low, and he says so—recalling vividly the heft of it.

Highly creative people can do this. They have a high degree of visual imagery. If the word "visual" tends to mean only something seen or imagined to be seen, then, let us say, they have a high degree of sense imagery—which includes all of the senses.

One of our very creative people is John Pierce, of Bell Telephone Laboratories. What of his imagination? It has helped him to make notable advances in electronics. He has written several books for the Science Study Series. But also, did you know that under the name of J. J. Coupling, he is a top-notch science fiction writer?

We heard earlier from Walkup of Battelle Memorial Institute. In another paper† he has emphasized the importance of the role of visualization in the creative process.

Walkup has asked people to visualize twenty-seven cubes, packed together to make one large cube. Then, if the big cube is painted all over, they are asked how many small cubes have been painted on zero, one, two, or three sides. There is a very wide range of response, depending on the ability of subjects to visualize the situation. He says:

> Inventors with whom I have talked report thinking visually about complex mechanisms and organic chemical molecules combining with other molecules. So, it appears that ideas which can be grasped when drawn on paper can be visualized without being put on paper, perhaps with many shorthand approximations for unimportant parts. Also, the nature of the *seeing* or sensing is peculiar. It is almost a *feeling like* the object being visualized. One can *feel* the pressure of contacting objects; or the erosion of material by friction; or the flow of heat from one point to another; or the swing of the oscillating electrical circuit; or the bending of light as it passes from one medium to another; or the appropriateness of a well-designed structure to hold a maximum load, with every part being equally strained in the process; or the eternal bouncing about of the molecules of a gas; or the almost physical transfer of energy from the gasoline, through the motor, transmission, and to the driving wheels of the automobile. It is as though one's own kinesthetic sensing mechanisms were associated with the physical object and that he thus sensed directly what was going on in the external system. In highly developed visualizers, this process probably is carried over for other than physical systems.

† Lewis E. Walkup, "Creativity in Science through Visualization," *Perceptual and Motor Skills* (Southern University Press, 1965).

Walkup finds that the highly creative inventors he has studied are highly competent visualizers: and they are so used to it that "they have never stopped to consider whether or not it is special" with them. When he asks them about using lifelike visualizations when inventing, he says they are prone to say, "Why yes. Doesn't everybody?"

Now, we have our differences in these matters, as in all others. The ability to visualize varies from person to person, in kind and in degree. A mathematician might be strong at visualizing symbols, numbers, and equations, but low at mechanisms. An interior decorator might do splendidly in form and color, but have lots of trouble in mentally subtracting 37 from 92.

A question, as yet unanswered, is: Can the ability to visualize be trained and increased to any considerable extent? Or is there a genetically determined capacity above which we cannot go, but below which we can fall for lack of use? It may be a long time before research finds the truth. In the meantime, the safe rule to follow would be to keep in practice. Do not let these mental capacities lapse: the capacity to form mental pictures; the capacity to feel, mentally, with the several senses, to get the mind right into the thing being studied.

A CLEAN-OUT DOOR THAT POPPED

"When John Alby Spencer was fifteen years old he was employed on the night shift of a little lumber camp in Northern Maine. His principal job was tending the fire in an old wood-burning steam boiler. The fuel burned so quickly that young Spencer had to step lively to keep his gauge up. Being an observant youth he noticed that when his fires were going nicely the old clean-out door would belly out with a loud report, and when cooled off would snap back into a concave position. This gave Spencer an idea—in fact, *the* idea. He placed a log against the door and awaited results. Sure enough, when his fires died down the versatile plate snapped back into shape and signalled its need for fuel by kicking the billet to the floor.

"Johnny Spencer carried the idea of the old clean-out door in his head for eighteen years, turning over the principle in his mind and searching for a practical use to make of that phenomenon. During those years Spencer acquired a thorough knowledge of mechanical engineering and after a decade of experiment, tinkering and studying, he worked out his idea in the form of a little bimetal disc known as the Spencer Control or Thermostat." (Quoted from a Spencer Thermostat Company booklet of 1929.)

Isn't it thrilling to think of how a fifteen-year-old makes an observation, stubbornly clings to it through eighteen years of preparation, and comes out with a real winner? A bimetallic disc.

In its unobtrusive way, bimetal is one of our very important and pervasive inventions. In one form or another, it quietly serves you to open and close electrical contacts in your home, to regulate the temperatures of rooms, refrigerators, range ovens, and electric irons; it serves you in many ways in industry. But to *use* bimetal properly demands invention and good engineering. Let us see why. Bimetal has long been known. If you take two narrow, flat, thin strips of different metals, exactly alike when cold, and heat them, unequal expansion rates will make one longer than the other. If riveted together, the combination will bend with heat. In practice they are actually welded together into a one-piece combination. That's bimetal. But there is a problem: As a bimetallic thermostat slowly heats up, the strip of bimetal slowly bends, and electrical contact points are slowly opened; likewise for closure of contact, on cooling.

Now, if you want to have so much contact trouble that you can't live with it, just do that very thing. In many applications, snap action is needed. Snap: open. Snap: closed. And repeat, thousands and thousands of times, without trouble. Much ingenuity has gone into inventing this or that mechanism, adding springs and such to turn that slow action of a bimetal strip into snap action, thereby adding complexity.

Then came Spencer, marrying the snap action of a clean-out door to bimetal. He did what no thermostat engineer had ever thought of: He made a *round* disc of bimetal, pressed into the form of a shallow dish. When heated, it buckled through itself at tremendous speed. When cooled, it buckled back. No springs, no gadgetry. Simplicity itself. Spencer named it Klixon. Not only does it give snap action to contacts, it has found wide use for opening and shutting gas valves in on-and-off applications. We shall continue the Spencer story in Chapter Thirteen.

EIGHT

Getting the Hands into the Act

Foreign students from certain areas coming to study engineering in this country sometimes have little background knowledge of even the most common materials and processes used by engineers. I have long known this, but was really shocked, some years ago, to find one in my class who had never soldered even one thing—and he was thirty years old. Soldering is a pretty personal thing, and you don't learn it out of books. If his inventory of knowledge about processes needed in electrical engineering was as meager as the sample indicates, what were the prospects of his becoming a good engineer—let alone becoming a creative engineer?

A vast amount of *learning* comes by way of the hands, and a vast amount of *doing* is done by the hands. I would therefore raise this question: Somewhere along the line in the creative process, should we deliberately get the hands into the act?

Manipulativeness seems to be the word preferred for the tendency to use the hands in the creative activity. Torrance, in *Scientific Creativity*, says, ". . . many writers have maintained that this is important in invention and scientific discovery."

As an experimentalist who likes to build things, I lean strongly toward getting my hands involved. Be warned that I am about to ride a pet idea in this chapter.

THE HANDS TEST

I told in the Introduction of asking twelve teaching colleagues, one by one, to look at five objects on a table, and make a model of something then being taught or that had been taught. Not one knew or suspected the real purpose of my test.

In each case, the subject soon reached for the objects, to pick up one or more. That ended the test. One man took twenty-five seconds. One took only two seconds. The typical score was around ten seconds. *They all got their hands into the act.* The reaching seemed automatic. My interpretation is that they all wanted to pick up the objects, get acquainted with them, manipulate them—to help them get ideas.

Seemingly, my simple "hands test" says that when a person is trying to be creative, he will get his hands into the act if he possibly can.

Children are highly creative and are speedy learners. They are great grabbers and handlers and feelers. They certainly get their hands into the act, whatever the act may be.

Anatomists will tell you that in the brain, the area devoted to sense impressions coming *from* the hands, and to motor control *of* the hands, is very large indeed, compared to other such areas. One of the respectable hypotheses concerning man's evolution is that the evolving of hands, able to carry things and to manipulate skillfully, preceded, and made possible, the development of the parts of the brain with which man thinks.

DUNCKER'S PENDULUM TEST

A very interesting test involving the hands is described in an article by E. W. Jackson.*

"Entering into the creative process comes another mysterious trick of the mind—the *ability to shift emphasis,* to

* "Be Creative" (*Family Circle,* July 1965).

change from one frame of reference to another. To demonstrate this, an eminent German psychologist, Karl Duncker [around 1930] asked some subjects to make a pendulum out of some ordinary objects, including a nail, and a cord with an attached pendulum weight. All they had to do was to drive a nail into the wall and then hang the cord with the pendulum attached. Half the subjects failed. They had no hammer. The other half cleverly saw how to use the pendulum weight as a hammer.

"In another experiment, Duncker gave other subjects a cord and weight *separately*. He did not say what the weight was for. All these subjects, not held back by preconceived notions, saw how to make double use of the weight—as a hammer *and* as a pendulum weight."

In the second test, some no doubt quickly jumped to the complete solution. It may be that others, temporarily stuck, fiddled around, hefted the weight, and in doing so, got the idea of driving the nail with it. This would all help to induce the pendulum idea to come.

Back to the first test, and those who failed: Could it be that most of them did more looking than trying? Without playing around with the weight, there could be an inadequate appreciation of its mass, and a failure to consider its use as a hammer.

FUNCTIONAL FIXEDNESS

The tests Duncker devised are called functional fixedness problems. When a familiar object is used in an unfamiliar or novel way, the person tested is being creative by getting around a block. To most of us most of the time, a hammer is a hammer, and only that. If it remains only that, and its function, as a hammer, remains fixed in mind, then we fail to think of using it in a new way.

Sam Glucksberg, who heads a group at Princeton University, has written a valuable article† on what he and others have found. Suppose you are tested by being given

† "Some Ways to Turn on New Ideas" (*Think*, March–April 1968), pp. 24–38.

some device to wire up. You get screws, wire, perhaps a cell and a switch and a buzzer, and a screwdriver. When you are all but finished, you find there isn't quite enough wire. If you can get around functional fixedness, it occurs to you to use the screwdriver as a conductor, to complete the connection. If not, you fail.

It is found that if you have been using the tool only as a screwdriver shortly before the test, its normal function is so firmly fixed that you may fail. Or again, language effect can enter in. If instructions for the test are handed you, including a picture of the screwdriver, and it is labeled as "screwdriver," you may block; but on the other hand, if instead it is labeled "gimmick" or called some other neutral term, your mind is freed to use it for novel purposes. In another test, a thumbtack box would have to serve to hold a candle. All of a group solved the problem when the box was presented empty. But if presented filled with thumbtacks, as many as 80 per cent of bright college students failed to make a candleholder out of it, even after half an hour of struggling.

THE POCKET KNIFE QUESTION

Many times in my experimental work, I have had to work up an improvement or create a technique. Time and again, I have picked up this part or that device; glared at it; laid it down; writhed and wriggled and squirmed; picked it up again; given up, and then come back to it to do that all over again. Many times I have asked myself the kind of question that I recently formed into the "pocket knife question."

You know these knives: The blade folds into the handle, and the back spring holds the blade there; when you open it, that same spring locks the blade in the open position. Imagine you are an inventor, but not of today. You are far enough back so that this spring idea has not been invented. You have a knife. It folds. But it has to rub against something to keep the blade in. When you open it, you have to put a pin in the hole to lock the blade open. And you ache to improve it. Assume that in the end, you do: You become the first inventor of the modern spring mechanism. Of course, when you start your creative effort, you have no idea whatever as to how this will all work out. But you start.

Going to extremes, I give you two choices, while struggling for ideas.

CHOICE ONE: *You will hold the knife, feel it, manipulate it, and so on.*
CHOICE TWO: *You will put the knife away and out of sight.*

Which should you do? To put it in startling terms, will Choice One operate to *stimulate* creativity, or oppositely, to *inhibit* it?

WHICH CHOICE? BOTH!

The more we read of how creative people operate as they themselves try to describe it, the more it seems like this: Each, in his own way, and in a manner appropriate to his project, first gets his hands into the act, then gets them out again.

Getting the hands into the act belongs to the preliminary phase of the creative process—the work phase—the conscious effort phase. Here, the problem and its nature are studied; ways and means of trying to solve it are considered; apparatus may be designed, or even built by the experimenter himself; experiments and tests may be run; data may be collected and reviewed; books may be consulted. There is a total immersion, a total commitment. There is a strong urge to get the desired concept, the brilliant inspiration: a conscious urge. But all of this activity is in the conscious realm—and the inspiration won't come. This is the business of holding the pocket knife, manipulating it, feeling it, looking at it. That's Choice One.

But then, as Langmuir and Helmholtz and many others have testified, the needed "flash of genius" typically comes. When? At oddest moments, *when doing something else un-*

related to the creative effort; and *not, typically,* when in touch with the physical situation itself. This corresponds to putting the knife away, and largely out of mind for the time being. That's Choice Two.

Long since, I learned the trick of "walking away from it." After dutifully and consciously struggling with the device, process, or whatnot in my laboratory, and apparently wasting my time, I get up and walk out. Go up the hall for mail. Or get on the bike and go for coffee. Every so often, the needed idea catches up with me.

To answer that question as best I can, I would say that Choice One both stimulates and inhibits. It stimulates interest, observation, and the desire to solve the problem. But as long as it is continued, it may inhibit the coming of the inspiration. After Choice One must come Choice Two, which may seem like giving up. But it isn't. We put the knife away, out of sight and largely out of the conscious mind. Later, we will go more fully into what seems to happen in this "do-nothing" period which ends with the flash of insight—the inspiration.

To get some good reactions to these ideas, I have put the "hands question" to three highly creative men, on an either-one-or-the-other basis, using the "pocket knife question" as the example. Choice One or Choice Two—which should it be? I did this without giving any hint that it really should be both. This served to bring out the excellent discussions that come next. I am much indebted to these three for taking the time to illuminate the subject.

In reading the discussions, you will note that for the most part, my contributors seem almost to be doing away with Choice One, and to question whether it is necessary "to get the hands into the act." I will discuss that after quoting from their letters.

WHAT WALKUP SAYS

Lewis E. Walkup of Battelle Memorial Institute has many patents to his name. The phenomenally successful

Xerox process owes much of its development to Walkup's inventive capacity. He writes,

> Your *hands question* is . . . complicated. I'll agree and disagree with you on the subject. I agree that all of the really creative persons I know have a good facility with the actual sizes and shapes of the things with which they are dealing; they know things and their properties. It is almost as if they have had to go through the stage of learning such practical properties of things. And, this is a real "gut" knowledge of things, not just their superficial aspects. Thus . . . these persons are not fooled by materials, they do not break screws when inserting them, they select the proper materials and elements of construction and, things that they build are "right" for the job. However—and this is a bit difficult to say—I do not think that this is a part of the creative process. In fact, I know a lot of lab technicians quite good in these areas, but who are not at all creative. I guess I am saying that this appreciation of things is a "necessary but not sufficient" property of creative persons. . . . I think that the secret ingredient (of creativity) is the ability and proclivity—almost incessant drive —to mentally manipulate and explore combinations of things. Of course, this may lead to (physically) trying out such combinations as result from such mental manipulations, but it does not necessarily do this. . . . Creativity is a mental "game" that some few persons play, whose rules are to try to think out new combinations of well-known materials and process elements that others are content to use just as they are. And, I would stress the meaning of "game" in this connection; for I think "play" and the attitude of playfully toying around with ideas is most important to successful creativity. The totally serious person will never let himself stray from the straight and narrow path of conservative thinking; he cannot afford the time to explore the unusual and the bizarre, in whose realms lie all of the things that will be accepted as the usual—once they have been discovered and invented; but not at all until that time. . . . Knowledge is of the utmost importance to creativity. Creativity is simply the combining of known

elements into new and useful arrangements. And, the process can only work with elements that are *known* to the person trying to create.

Dr. Gordon K. Teal, Assistant Vice President of Texas Instruments, has a phenomenal record. In 1967, he received the Inventor of the Year Award as presented by the PTC Research Institute. When at Bell Laboratories, his work in growing crystals and other contributions did much to make it possible for transistors to become realities. He says,

I feel that my hands have very little to do with the inventions I have made. Perhaps the use of my hands in connection with the experimental work has given me some feeling for the practicality of certain ideas, but I don't see that the use of the hands is directly involved in my inventions. For other people, it may be different. . . . Frequently, I don't have the feeling of my hands being involved nearly so much as my head and brains. To me, my invention seems directly related to the process of visualizing beyond what I can actually see and imagining what might be. . . . I have some real difficulty in connecting this very directly with the influence of my hands.

My third contributor, Dr. James M. Lafferty, is Manager, General Physics Laboratory, at General Electric Company. He comments,

I too have an interest in creativity, and the *hands question* is an interesting one. I believe that when you are young, working with your hands is a very vital part of training, and it helps to develop a *feel* for things. However, as you grow older and acquire this *feel*, you are likely to spend your valuable time in thinking and sketching, and leave the actual construction of your invention to others. I suppose different people operate in different ways.

Creativity requires vision. This usually occurs in one's mind, however it may be supplemented by . . . sketches or by making physical models. To be an inventor one first must know what is needed. He then brings all of his previous experience to bear on the problem. The broader his experience, the better. He then thinks and tries to envision in his own mind what the consequences would be of approaching the problem in various ways. He then makes a judgment as to the best approach. What happens then depends on how complicated this situation is. Perhaps if the device is simple enough the entire invention can be thought through in one's mind. Usually, however, the inventor will have to make simple sketches to help clarify his thinking. He will then build or have built for him a model which he will test and evaluate to see if it performs in accordance with his thinking. If his *feel* for the situation has been good, little modification will be needed. However, if he has had little experience with the subject, major modifications are likely to be required.

In order to acquire this intuitive feel for how things work, the inventor must have familiarity with the subject which he has acquired by keen observation of similar situations in the past. This intuitive feel for how things will function is not necessarily transmitted through the finger tips but rather comes through careful observation. While it is not necessary for the individual to actually build his invention with his own hands, he must design it on paper or transmit his thoughts to someone who can. He will then want to follow its construction in great detail and actually participate in tests and operation of his invention, for this is how he builds up his storehouse of knowledge and experience and how he acquires a feel for what will happen when he mentally creates his next invention.

All three of these very creative men have long since had so much experience with physical things that they no longer need to get the hands into the preliminary, conscious phase: They can perfectly well visualize a valve, an electrode, a vacuum chamber, and so on.

Next, all three have done much of their creative work by dealing with the unseen. How do you see an electron? You don't, and never will. Yet these men have had to deal with unseen electrons, unseen ions, unseen monolayers on surfaces, unseen gases clinging to surfaces or dissolved in metals, unseen current flow, unseen forces. Without an active imagination, and an ability to form some kind of mental picture of the unseen, they could never have done what they did. When Niels Bohr produced his model of the atom, did he first *observe* electrons whizzing around the nucleus? Impossible. He had the originality to postulate it, then visualize it, then test it theoretically to see if the concept was any good.

Now, back to Walkup, Teal, Lafferty, so well grounded in experimental things that they no longer need to get the hands into the act: Suppose I find a fourth man. Let's say he is equal, creatively, to any one of the three. I invite him to the Canadian island where I use a chain saw to bring down trees for firewood. Suppose he has never used an ax, and has never even seen one. I take him to the eighteen-inch pine behind the cabin. I show him one of those little Boy Scout axes. I tell him that axes can be used to cut down trees. He agrees. I then say, "If you think this is the right tool for cutting down this tree, say so; if not, please turn loose with your creativity and describe a better one—but of the same general kind." Having seen the tree and the ax and heard the problem would he then turn, enter the cabin, ask for pencil and paper, and go to work? He could not. He lacks experience. He lacks data. You know what he would do. He has to get some experience he has missed out on. He would reach for that poor little ax and start swinging.

After some strokes, he would not even be through the bark. If he got through that, he would find the going tougher yet. With experience gained, he might be ready to sketch an improved tool, with a longer handle, a wider blade, a heavier head—to make a one-handed ax more suited for the job. So much for improvement. Later on he might even go creative and invent a two-handed ax, so that the greater energy per stroke would bring down a tree with fewer strokes.

To sum up: Even the highly experienced researcher, faced with a situation quite foreign to his experience, may have to get into the laboratory, or factory, or outdoors, to learn new elements at firsthand.

The young, inexperienced creative person has no choice: He must familiarize himself with every part of the situation, and this can't be done just by being brilliant. There is no substitute for experience. If some of that requires getting the hands into the act, it must be done.

THE FAILURE OF THE GREEKS

We are indebted to the Greeks and the Romans for much of our cultural heritage. So much so, in fact, that we tend to overestimate the Greek contribution to science, and to overlook their shortcomings. The Greeks in the Golden Age had keen minds and used them. They used them for argument and reasoning. In some ways, they were keen observers. They were curious about man and his environment. They had ideas. They did make some admirable contributions to science. At the same time, they promulgated, and clung to plenty of just plain foolish ideas that did the cause of science no good. Why?

They did not get their hands into the act. Some did, but they were few indeed. The Greeks, mainly, were not experimentalists. They had slaves, and slaves did the work. There were freemen who also engaged in manual effort, but their standing in Greek cultural circles was low indeed. For these reasons and perhaps others, the Greek philosopher-scientist considered it beneath his dignity, not fitting to his station in life, to do things with his hands.

This attitude is very well brought out by what the *Encyclopaedia Britannica* says of Archimedes: "He himself set no value on the ingenious mechanical contrivances that made him famous, regarding them as beneath the dignity of pure science and even declining to leave any written record of them."

Thus it was that the way the Greeks established their science was to observe with the eyes, then erect hypotheses, then argue, use "reason," and reach conclusions. With the evidence so incomplete, it is no wonder that many conclusions were ludicrous.

It might be held that they were so lacking in materials, tools, and ways to build apparatus, that a desire to experiment would have been frustrated anyway. Not so. They had a full capacity to invent machines and gadgets, and they had a pretty fair technology established. This is amply shown in a book by Robert S. Brumbaugh.‡

Why then did not the Greek scientist build—or have built —some apparatus for putting his ideas to the test? He wasn't interested. Such work was beneath him: Leave the invention of gadgets to those mechanics in the lower levels of the Greek society.

They might have done plenty. They had water clocks. Therefore, by using the echo method I used in that long hall, they could easily and pretty accurately have measured the speed of sound in air. They had cliffs they could have used, to find whether a little rock and a large boulder would or would not fall together. How much apparatus would it take to work out the law of the pendulum? A string and a weight and a water clock. Not much! But without the gumption to stop arguing and *try* it, it didn't get done. They had amber and lodestone and knew a little about both. Did any Greek ever so much as float a piece of lodestone on a shingle, and discover that it would swing around to point in a particular way? No: The world had to wait a long time for that.

‡ *Ancient Greek Gadgets and Machines* (New York: Thomas Y. Crowell Company, 1966).

NINE

Methods and Guidelines

The more we learn about the creative process, the more certain it is that there are not, and never can be, fixed, clear-cut, hard-and-fast rules to guide us along every step, in any kind of case, from problem to discovery or invention. The complexity of modern science guarantees that there be wide variations from one project to the next. In one case, the important hunch may be the very idea that starts the whole creative process; in another, it may be impossible for that hunch to appear until a lot of new work is done; in a third, creativity arises from an unpredictable, accidental observation. Then if we add the differences between men: some strongly theoretical, others strongly experimental, we have a different kind of variation. And then some, taking up a problem, are already very familiar with the area concerned; others, on their problems, are not, but the fresh approach they bring may be the very factor needed to develop the necessary intuitions.

TWO WIDELY DIFFERENT MEN

A Swiss patent office clerk worked in his spare time, with paper and pencil and his mind. He was not a professional scientist. In 1905, he published the *Special Theory of Relativity*. His name was Albert Einstein.

A few years later at General Electric Company, W. D. Coolidge became the first to find a way to make tungsten ductile. He was not a metallurgist; he was a professional chemist. He worked in a laboratory, as Einstein did not. His method succeeded because it controlled grain shape and size—but theory had not predicted this. After Coolidge had his success, the metallurgists moved in to make intensive studies, and then the broad principles of grain growth pertaining to all metals were worked out.

These two great contributions came from two very different men. One, using imagination and profound insight, worked theoretically. The other, in his laboratory, achieved his immediate goal, and unexpectedly opened the door to a great advance in metallurgy.

It is perfectly plain that there will never be a Creativity Guidebook, so organized and indexed that we could always turn to the right section and be told what to do, or think about, next. There are, however, some general methods and guidelines that apply to many or perhaps most creative situations.

YOU ALWAYS START FROM WHERE YOU ARE

Suppose you have gasoline money for one day of travel. If you are in your car in Texas and have to get to Boston, you might say, "If I were only in New York, I could make it." Likewise, if you are seventeen, and want to design the world's best satellite, you could say, "If only I had a couple of degrees and ten years of experience, I could." The New York-to-Boston "if" is merely wishful thinking. The "if" about the satellite need not be. For one thing, it shows that you know the score: At seventeen, lacking knowledge, experience, and judgment, you might design the world's worst satellite. But if you stick to that goal, read all you can on the subject (from where you are), and keep on until you get the needed training, you might design the best.

One way to start from where you are is to go to your favorite gasoline station. Look it *all* over. Find something you think could be improved or replaced by something better. There are hand tools, special tools, grease-gun systems, hoists, pumps, ways for cleaning windshields, shelf devices for displaying items for sale, the cash register and the record system, and more. Now this is true: A lot of smart people got ahead of you, to perfect these items and devices and systems. Don't let that get you down. You really might come up with a good idea, starting from where you are, and with little new knowledge needed to work it out. The chances are against it, but so what? In chasing an idea that doesn't turn out, you may learn a lot about packaging, or transport, or mass manufacture, or of human limitations that require a device to be made so that any temporary helper can operate it. Many a creative man has found his life's work just by getting interested in some such matter, going deeper into it, becoming more interested, and then turning himself into an expert.

Inherently, creativity tends to put us squarely up against things we are not prepared to do. To attempt to create is to try to bring into being the hitherto unknown. A crack research team is handed a goal. It also has to start from where it is. In a highly complex case, the way to achieving it may mean first, reading many references to see if the thing has already been done, and to get valuable information and hunches that may help. Costly equipment may have to be ordered and assembled and broken in. A batch of new learning may have to be absorbed. Several promising lines of investigation may be started. When the team leader took on the project, was the team all set to go to work? Anything but! It had to get itself prepared, first.

When Samuel Morse learned on that ocean trip that electricity travels fast, he didn't wait. He at once began to try to invent the telegraph. He was so ignorant about electricity and magnetism that he didn't know how ignorant he was —and a man is in bad shape when he is that way. But he started. It took him years of slow and painful endeavor, but he got there, didn't he?

THE SCIENTIFIC METHOD

The scientific method is a method that deserves great credit for what it has done and can do, to make progress in science. Some teachers are inclined to give it much emphasis. Beware! If they themselves are not creative (as may happen), they may, by that very emphasis, be putting you onto a method that *can* be totally unproductive. This does not mean you will avoid it. You will use it, and must. But as you will see, you must use it at times, and completely abandon it at other times. It is the method of logic, of reason. I will give you Walkup's version of it, taken from his paper, "Individual Creativity in Research."

This won't be easy reading. You may have to come back to it a few times to let it soak in.*

1. A problem is defined for which one is to seek a solution.
2. An hypothesis is advanced, stating a possible solution.
3. Predictions are made from this hypothesis relative to the facts of nature in the area of the problem.
4. Pertinent data are gathered in the area of these predictions.
5. The data are used to "test" or "prove" the predictions and, thereby, to test the hypothesis.
6. Conclusions are drawn as to the validity of the hypothesis and as to its usefulness in solving the problem and in extending our knowledge of nature.

The scientific method will now be applied in a particular case.

HOLES IN POLES

By 1856, Morse's telegraph was coming into wide use. It saw much service by the North in the Civil War, and then its use rapidly expanded. Then came Bell's telephone, about 1878. Whereupon something new appeared in vast numbers: telegraph and telephone poles. Seasoned wood poles, with the bark skinned off. Then a problem arose. Here and there, it was noted that up near the tops, *holes* an inch or so across and perhaps twice as deep would appear. What caused the holes? Undoubtedly, the cause became known at once, but

* For more about the scientific method, consult the *Encyclopaedia Britannica*.

let us play the game out. We apply the scientific method, using Walkup's outline.

The problem—what makes the holes—has been defined (Step 1). A man is assigned to work on the problem. He needs hypotheses, so he thinks of three (Step 2): carpenter ants do it; or it is just a matter of rotting; or there were hidden cavities to begin with, and weathering uncovered them. The facts of nature (Step 3) are next investigated. Data are gathered (Step 4) about carpenter ants, about wood rot, and about trees growing with internal cavities.

The man finds that carpenter ants do not make such holes. Neither does rot. Nor do trees grow with such cavities.

The scientific method screeches to a dead halt. It has been useful in eliminating three useless hypotheses. It has been useless in solving the problem. A new start is needed.

WHAT MAKES THE HOLES, AND WHY?

Then someone suggests a wild idea. Woodpeckers! This is a *new* hypothesis (Step 2). A prediction is made relative to the facts of nature (Step 3) and it holds up: yes woodpeckers *can* make such holes.

But suppose the man does know something about woodpeckers, but not everything. He continues with the scientific method. He gathers data (Step 4) but does so, not in the field, but from what he knows and thinks he knows. He knows that most of the holes are too small for woodpecker nests. He knows these seasoned poles do not harbor the grubs that the birds drill for. And he *thinks* he knows that drilling holes is hard work for the woodpecker. So (Step 5) he uses the data to test that hypothesis, and what is the outcome? He uses the scientific method to blow up the correct hypothesis. Don't blame the method. Blame him.

Then some other chap comes along who is willing to admit that he doesn't know *all* about woodpeckers. He goes into the field (Step 4) and *sees* woodpeckers happily drilling these "useless" holes.

By all means, note this: The scientific method, in his hands, did lead to the goal, after the right hunch came along, and after adequate observations were made.

Note this also: That first fellow who assumed that drilling holes is hard work for a woodpecker—what right did he have to make any such assumption? Was he ever a woodpecker?

Well, the problem got solved. Woodpeckers make the holes. But that brings on two new problems. First, can a practical, inexpensive way be found for stopping the fool woodpecker from ruining the poles? And next, for the curious biologist, why does the woodpecker do it? Maybe it does it for fun. Or again, many birds use song to warn trespassers away from their territory. Perhaps the woodpecker picks the most resonant pole he can find to hammer out that warning. (We once had a woodpecker around home that came every day to hammer on our eaves trough, making a horrible din.) This is where you come in. Neither problem has been solved!

The scientific method is all-important, and must be used time and again in the creative process. But it does not encourage the hunch. When used with insufficient information, or insufficient humility, it can condemn the very hunch, or hypothesis, that would turn out to be correct.

ARE YOU WILLING TO TAKE A CHANCE?

That is, are you willing to be wrong sometimes? If so, you can join the Creativity Club. The fellow who always wants to be right will never be creative. When he makes a mistake, he is ashamed of it. The creative man makes a mistake, and he says, "That's all right—I've made lots of them; I have played many a hunch that turned out wrong, but so what? Those that turn out right are the winners; and in this game, you can't always be right!"

Risk-taking: that is what some writers call it. A friend of mine who runs a research group was recently given a million-dollar grant for furthering government research in a certain area. Does this mean there is no risk—that everyone is sure that when the million is spent, certain discoveries and developments, guaranteed in advance, will be forthcoming? It means nothing of the sort. The hope is there, so is the competence, the energy, and the effort. But no man can *guarantee* the outcome of real research. That is one aspect of risk-taking, of being willing to gamble and be wrong.

This means sometimes taking a chance on those hunches. Intuition tells you that your creative goal can be reached by a certain line of approach. Intuition is enormously important, for out of it often comes the very approach needed, when reason may say, "This doesn't look good at all." But again, intuition can be wrong, and there is no way of telling that until it is somehow followed up. This reminds me of once when I was desperately in need of hunches. First, I had invented a way to cast plaster on wet paper strips laid on plate glass—to get a series of gentle steps on the surface on a fluid mapper slab. This was a real advance. But trouble developed: Sometimes a dimple formed in the slab surface. Mysterious! I worked at that mystery for two solid weeks, trying out twenty-eight different ways of getting rid of those dimples (following one hunch after another) and with no success. As it turned out, I was working completely in the dark all that time, quite unaware of a couple of phenomena that really were the cause. The final, and successful hunch, was to rig a mirror so that I could look up through the plate glass and *see* a dimple forming. Then the light began to dawn, and the causes were found and eliminated.

One of the qualities most essential to the creative individual is a willingness to take risks, and to guess wrong. The open mind, with a desire to strike out in any direction—even to questioning accepted beliefs—must be a part of that bag of tricks from which we eventually bring success.

Dr. M. H. Albert has written a short article, "On the Importance of Making Mistakes."† Below, R & D stands for research and development. He says:

If there is one thing that distinguishes R & D workers from those in most other areas of human endeavor, it is this: R & D people *should* make mistakes. Most of us, from the age of six onwards, are ingrained with the idea of doing

† *Research/Development*, April 1967, p. 25.

things correctly, and the attitude sticks with us throughout our careers. Indeed, the whole fabric of our society is repelled by mistakes. . . . Distaste for error is logical, meaningful, and desirable in most walks of life. We don't want, and don't need goofs! *But error is an essential part of the creative process!* One cannot be truly original or creative without making errors; lots of them, in fact. . . . I do not suggest that sloppiness, carelessness, or stupidity should be excused. I do say that errors should be understood to be an essential part of the R & D process, and that the researcher should be judged on the final results which he obtains, not on how many test-tubes he has broken on the way.

The man who always wants to be right never creates anything!

THE CUT-AND-TRY METHOD

In Mitchell Wilson's wonderful book‡ he tells the story of how Goodyear tried to make India rubber useful: that is, as we now say, how to vulcanize it. In the pure cut-and-try method, you just cut loose and try anything that seems to offer some hope; or even try blindly. Goodyear produced the classic case of doing just that. He tried everything he could get his hands on—blindly. Knowing no organic chemistry, what else could he do? So he stumbled on and on, finally came to trying sulphur as an additive, and vulcanized rubber was born.

Photography went through its birth struggles when nearly everything its inventors needed to know, was not known. Beaumont Newhall's book* on the discovery of photography, at the hands of Daguerre, Talbot, and others, should be read by all. Persistent men, working under great handicaps and using the cut-and-try method, laboriously

‡ *American Science and Invention* (New York: Bonanza Books, 1960).

* *Latent Image* (New York: Doubleday & Company, Inc., 1967).

brought a new art into being. But it was the only method they had! And it worked.

With the advances in science made since those times, a great deal of cutting-and-trying is no longer necessary. This knowledge, plus the scientific method, tells us perhaps, to try acids, not alkalis; or try high pressures in some process; and so on. That is, we may now know that success may come from some broad classification of material or process, and not probably from any other. Thus, guidelines can often be established. But often, that is as far as knowledge, plus the scientific method, will carry us. We then have to take over, and cut-and-try in some form must still prevail.

CONVERGENT AND DIVERGENT THINKING

These terms are much in the minds of some students of creativity. To put it in the extreme, a convergent thinker narrows down to reach his objective, while the divergent thinker explodes in all directions. This is just one kind of description. Let us go on.

Those adolescents in Chapter Three come into this picture. The high I.Q. students were *convergent*, in making conservative occupational choices, writing conservative themes, and so on; the creative students were *divergent*, in selecting a variety of occupations (some a bit "wild"), and showing a rich imagination in their picture-stimulated themes.

Another distinction: Conservatively sticking to the scientific method is convergent; willingness to cut-and-try is divergent. Still another: A scientist, trained in certain "established" beliefs and concepts, is convergent when he directs his research to discover something new *within that same framework;* and possibly, to find further "proof" that the framework is supportable. Another scientist is divergent when he is willing to question the basic assumptions, and may even try to upset the framework.

There is the natural tendency to assume that we are either the one or the other; and, going to extremes, to think of the (convergent) scholar who knows much but does not create;

PLATE 9   Bell Telephone Laboratories at Murray Hill, New Jersey. One of the world's most successful centers for creativity. (*Photograph from Bell Telephone Laboratories*)

PLATE 10   Arthur P. Frigo, and the elliptical pool table he invented.

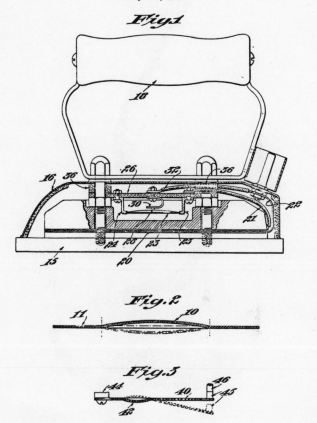

Fig.1

Fig.2

Fig.3

Witness

M.E.Organ

Inventor

John A. Spencer

by his attorneys

Van Everen Fish Holidat & Roy

PLATE 11   Spencer's patent, showing his bimetallic disc as used to regulate the temperature of an electric iron.

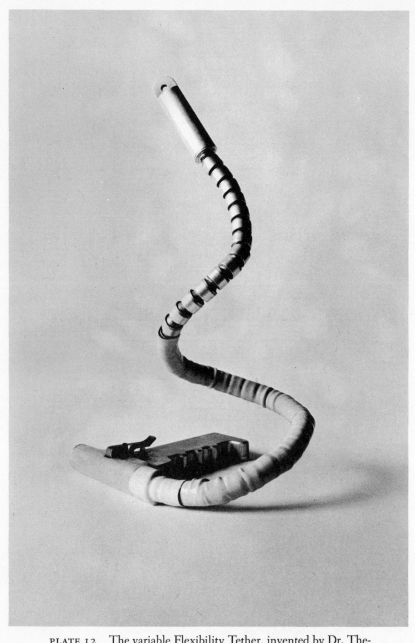

PLATE 12   The variable Flexibility Tether, invented by Dr. Theodore Marton.   (*Courtesy of General Electric Company*)

PLATE 13 The electrostatics section of the author's laboratory at the University of Michigan.

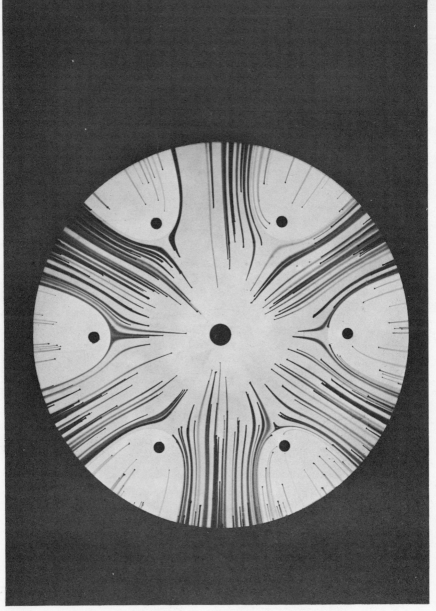

PLATE 14   A fluid mapper, simulating the electric field in a tri-
ode (a vacuum tube). (*Courtesy of* Scientific American)

PLATE 15 Vincent J. Schaefer (left), the first man to do cloud seeding from an airplane. Here, he is doing dry ice seeding in Yellowstone National Park, where he directs various lines of research every winter.

PLATE 16 Dr. James M. Lafferty, Manager of the General Physics Laboratory at General Electric Company, with the High-Power Vacuum Interruptor he and his group developed. Dr. Lafferty has 54 patents to his name.

as against the (divergent) inventor who cares little for great learning, but yearns to give the world something new. These are, of course, dangerous simplifications. Some hold that both kinds of thinking are required in the same man, at different times and stages in his creative process. Take E. O. Lawrence and the cyclotron. He may have been divergent when he got the cyclotron concept. When it came to having it made, he had to go convergent: getting down to cases, using available materials, getting the engineering done right, and having an instrument that worked.

SIMPLICITY VS. COMPLEXITY

An all-important guideline in creative work is to keep thinking simple rather than complex. Likewise for physical things: Keep them simple, not complicated.

The modern car is a magnificent monstrosity. Driven by an internal combustion engine, it has been improved by a host of ingenious men to the point where it is of truly admirable design. It is economical to run, it is durable, it has great flexibility of performance. Yet its hundreds of parts represent a regrettable compromise with two facts: You can carry a lot of energy in gasoline, and the engine runs on gasoline. Many are aware of the fact that if a new type of storage battery could also pack in the necessary energy, the electric automobile would be so much simpler than what we have now that there would be no comparison. That battery must be light enough, low enough in cost, and last long enough; and it should, perhaps, carry us for 200 miles in hilly country on a charge. (Of course, the fuel cell instead of the battery, may turn out to be the answer.)

Suppose we could bring back two men, at the peak of their powers: Michael Faraday and Benjamin Franklin. We ask them to review modern technology and the history of the automobile's development; and then to report any impressions they have. They might say something like this: "Gentlemen, when we view a Cadillac, we are filled with amazement and admiration. It is a wonderful machine. We are also shocked by its complexity. Complexity, in and of itself, is no proper goal. It so often represents a temporary compromise to be lived with, until a higher ingenuity replaces it with simplicity. Perhaps the simpler electric car will become feasible, perhaps not. Time will tell. We admire your *present* interest in the electric car. But why, tell us please, have you so *belatedly* started to do your research in a big way? Did you get in a groove—the groove of improving the complex?"

I would pick that committee for good reason. In all the history of science, the two men who stand above all others in the genius needed to conceive and build *simple* experiments to prove or disprove an idea, were Faraday and Franklin.

Time and again, good ingenuity has made a workable but complex device: then later, higher ingenuity has improved it by simplifying it. This is not an invariable rule, of course. But this does seem to be true: When we first think of a way to do or make something new, we tend to think of the hard ways first.

The early English railways had a complex, costly scheme for fastening the rails down to granite blocks. Along came the American, Robert Stevens, who invented the T-rail, the fishplate, the hooked spike, and the wood tie laid on a crushed rock roadbed. Much simpler, much cheaper, much better—and adopted worldwide within ten years.

One guideline for any problem is to try to simplify, not complicate it.

REVERSING AN IDEA

One of the approaches to some part of a problem is to reverse an idea: Turn it backward, or upside down, and see what happens. Often, in a device, there will be unwanted effects that can be reduced, but never eliminated. We worry about how much they may affect strength, or efficiency, or whatever. Friction offers an example. The worry: Perhaps bearing friction will use up a large part of the power developed by an electric motor. Put the worry in reverse: Think of *trying* to use up that power, by making the motor drive idle shafts running in plenty of bearings. It would take a lot of useless bearings to do it.

Or consider the hostess. She fills a teapot with boiling water in the kitchen, carries it thirty-five feet, and places it on the tea table to make tea for guests. May it not be too cold by then? Reverse: Suppose you hope it will be cold enough by then to let you take a drink from it without getting burned. Don't try it!

You are making an experimental device that requires a shaft, and you must file a flat place on the shaft to take a set screw. You want to clamp the shaft firmly in the smooth jaws of a vise. But you worry: Maybe that will flatten the shaft—make it out-of-round. Reverse: Think of trying to flatten it that way! Try it and see.

Let's remind ourself of Speed again, and the too-sticky crude oil that didn't want to be pumped. We all think oil as a lubricant for other things. But Speed's problem was to lubricate the oil itself—and he did it with a water film. That was a beautiful example of reversal.

Time and again, when there is an unjustified worry, or hope, proper judgment comes to the rescue when you reverse or invert the thinking.

THE STIFF PLIERS

As a freshman in 1911 at Carnegie Tech, I was required to take a course in electric wiring. When the stockroom issued our tools, the pliers I got were so stiff in the joint that they had to be pulled open. They were a nuisance. So I had an idea. I went to the head of the shop course—an excellent machine shop man—and told him I was hoping to work some carborundum dust into the joint, with some oil, and loosen it up. What did he think? He was properly horrified. I was given a stern lecture about keeping grit *out* of bearings and plier joints. I left and did it anyway.

It turned a useless tool into a fine tool. He went on the principle that you never put grit into a bearing unless you get it all out again. I realize now, after all these years, that I reversed that rule, in an appropriate case. For the grit stayed in. However, this wasn't a journal bearing, due to turn endlessly and be ruined. Instead, years of service would actually give the joint very little chance to wear enough to be loose.

Last year a couple of boys of around eleven came over to our Canadian cabin to pay a call. I remembered a puzzler from my boyhood, got out the checkerboard, and turned them loose on it.

You are given eight checkers. The board has eight rows and eight columns. The problem: Place the checkers so that no two are in any one row or column; no two are in any diagonal; and no three are on a straight line. Time and again you think you have it, only to find that the third rule is violated. Wayne and Jimmy went to work. And if ever two boys had totally different methods, they did. Yes, their methods, technically, were the same: cut-and-try, for both. But their methods for action were different. Wayne was serious; Jimmy, aimlessly impulsive. When Wayne might nearly have had it, Jimmy would reach in and mess it all up.

Wayne went at it creatively. After getting the thing started, he began to get familiar with the problem, and tried to foresee the effect of a change. He did not take too long before trying it, finding he was stuck, and starting fresh again. He finally solved it, in spite of Jimmy's nuisance value.

This is a fine puzzler for our purposes here, because it will yield either to the cut-and-try method plus a little insight, or to the scientific method. As a child, I worked it by the scientific method, years and years before I had ever heard of that method. I put all checkers in the bottom row. I let the end one at the left alone. I advanced the next one up its column, but only as far as would avoid violating a rule. Likewise for the next, and so on. If no solution came, I knew that in starting over again, I should advance that first one by one square, and so on. If no solution came, start again and advance it again. I found that there were two possible solutions. (There may appear to be more, but by a single or double rotation, they all come down to two.)

This puzzler illustrates how a research goal may be reached either by cut-and-try; or by inexorable, time-consuming logic. Sometimes some guided cut-and-try, plus insight, can slash through to a solution long before the plodding-logic method could bring it in—if ever.

TEN

Steps in the Creative Process

In describing and naming the recognized steps in the creative process, we let Walkup speak again. Note that he draws upon a landmark book,* first published in 1950, by W. I. B. Beveridge, an animal pathologist. If a person interested in research and discovery was shipwrecked and had only one book to read, it should not be mine, or any other I know of —it should be Beveridge's. He has brought together many statements from Ehrlich, Pavlov, Helmholtz, Pasteur, Kelvin, and others. When we find other writers quoting some of these, they will often be drawing on Beveridge as a source. By all means read him, sooner or later.

Since Beveridge wrote, more and more literature on creativity has appeared, and it accelerates in volume. One reference leads to others. You can break into the literature almost anywhere, and go on from there.

THE STEPS

Walkup, in that paper, "Creativity in Science through Visualization," writes as follows:

"First, there are those who attempt to describe in words the gross features of the creative act as seen from outside the creative person. They finally agree, as has been illustrated elegantly (Beveridge, 1957), on the now-familiar steps in the creative process: (1) a problem is sensed and (2) rele-

* W. I. B. Beveridge, *The Art of Scientific Investigation* (New York: Vintage Books, 1957, 3rd ed.).

vant data are gathered. (3) Logical thinking goes as far as it can in trying to solve the problem, but the problem is not solved and there follows (4) a period of frustration, perhaps more appropriately called tantalization, because it is pleasant rather than unpleasant, but nothing seems to be happening. This period is followed by (5) the so-called flash of insight, and eventually, by (6) some process of verification."

This six-step description can be shortened by grouping the first three steps into one, "preparation." Many writers prefer the shortened description, with names as follows:

1. Preparation
2. Incubation
3. Illumination
4. Verification

PREPARATION

There is tremendous variety in the preparation phase. It can range from the simple instance of a boy trying to find better ammunition than pebbles for his slingshot (eventually adopting marbles); on up to the costly experimental struggles of a giant corporation in finding how to process titanium into needed shapes and forms.

Let us return to Speed, and the Bakersfield oil that was too mean and sticky to be pipelined to the coastal refineries. The problem: how to pipe it there *anyway?* In the preparation phase or step, Speed would consciously try for a solution. Heat the oil, to thin it; but how to keep a pipeline hot for miles? Thin it with something, such as naphtha or gasoline; but at too high a cost. Other schemes might come to mind, to be considered and rejected. Here is a man, consciously trying by the scientific method to solve his problem and meeting frustration. But he is totally immersed; he wants to do this thing. By seeking various alternatives he is preparing his mind to bring in the winner—which, admittedly, sometimes comes during the preparation phase, but usually will not. The frustration continues.

Note this also: Speed was already thoroughly familiar with oil, pipelines, and pumping stations. That is, much of his preparation was already in his background. A newcomer to the art, trying to solve this problem, would have a good deal of preliminary learning to do as part of *his* preparation.

INCUBATION

This is the period, long or short, of tantalizing frustration, when "nothing seems to be happening." If long, it is also, as Crane has said earlier in this book, when we may need "booster shots": occasional returns to the active, conscious effort. In these returns, the work so far is reviewed; a device is operated again; an obstinate part needing simplifying is handled, glared at, inspected; or a process that goes wrong is allowed to go wrong again.

Otherwise, in incubation, a part of the mind remains busy with the problem. The "flash of insight" is incubating. Earlier, we have had some creative men tell us of their thorough, hard work in the preparation phase; but no matter how thorough, and irrespective of conscious concentration, the inspiration did not come. After a period of incubation, the inspiration often unexpectedly arrived.

What goes on in this mysterious phase of incubation, and how does the mind, as we might say, manage itself to get the answer for us? This intensely interesting question is taken up in Chapter Twelve.

By the way, in those returns to the preparation phase above, did it strike you as a waste of time to let a process that goes wrong, go wrong again? It didn't strike Baekeland that way. When he set out to make a good material from phenol and formaldehyde, he was trying to do what others had failed at. He carefully looked up all of the unsuccessful experiments of the past twenty-five years, and repeated them. They all failed again! Then he went on to add three modifications, and with the birth of Bakelite, he gave the Plastics Age its biggest push ahead.†

† The Plastics Age, by the way, is one century old. Ivory for billiard balls was in short supply, the cost was rising, and a ten-

ILLUMINATION

Charles Darwin worked for years and years, collecting an immense volume of data bearing on the problem of evolution, and trying his best to bring it together into a unifying theory. There is no other case on record of such prolonged and thorough preparation. Then one day, when relaxed, and completely removed from his working place, the key issues, such as gradual change, the struggle for survival, and the survival of the fittest, fell into place. In his autobiography, Darwin tells exactly where and when the illumination took place.

Alfred Russell Wallace was also working on the evolution problem. He was then a third of the way around the world, spending eight years collecting specimens in the Malay Archipelago. He fell ill with a fever. After a few days of that, his illumination came, while still a very sick man. He worked out the main structure of his evolution argument —and in terms so like Darwin's, that Darwin said Wallace's section headings were much like Darwin's own.

Poincaré has told of two instances in his mathematical discoveries. In both cases, he had been through preparation with hard, conscious, but apparently fruitless work. Then came incubation. Then, when entirely removed in place and thought from his working situation, the illuminations came "out of thin air"; *and* he was perfectly sure that the answers were sound, and only needed later verification.

When Speed's illumination came, it might have been in two stages. First, lubricate the oil by sliding it within a film of water—if that could be managed. Second, rifle the pipeline, and let the rotation of the fluids automatically throw the denser water to the outside.

---

thousand-dollar prize was offered for a substitute. A printer, John Wesley Hyatt, son of a blacksmith, went to work. He mixed camphor, nitrocellulose, and solvents and invented celluloid, about 1868. That started the Plastics Age.

VERIFICATION

Verification means testing the inspiration in some adequate way. That pipeline again: Speed, no doubt, was quite sure his idea would work, but would it work *well* enough? He verified it by building that pilot model in his backyard. His success with that made it pretty certain that it would work at full scale—and it did, for shorter distances.

Not every hunch is sound. Intuition can be wrong at times. A flash of insight can be defective. A complicated mechanical device is being perfected, but it is stalled at a certain point. The inventor has gone through preparation and incubation. Then comes illumination. His troubles are over! But are they? Perhaps not until he makes a drawing does he find that his bright idea makes Part X interfere with Part Y, and no getting around it. No verification! He starts over again.

Or the researcher carries through on his problem, only to find that it was the wrong problem. At General Electric, Coolidge had succeeded at making tungsten wire ductile enough to be drawn into filaments for incandescent lamps; but at first they still broke too easily. Langmuir had an idea: that gas, trapped in the tungsten, weakened it. His problem, then, was to measure the amount of gas evolved when the lamp was burned and the filament was hot. To his surprise, he found at the end of two days that the originally evacuated bulb held gas equal to 7000 times the filament's volume—and it was still appearing! His idea was wrong, and his problem was wrong. So then, here was a *new* problem. Whence came all that gas? This led to his discovery that if the glass bulb was not heated for a long time in a vacuum, water vapor would come from its surface to react with the tungsten and produce hydrogen. And then? Further work enabled him to produce the gas-filled bulb, thereby giving the country a saving of a million dollars per day.

"I'LL SLEEP ON IT"

The wisdom of the ages has a way of ending up in a saying, such as, "I'll sleep on it." There is a tough situation to be faced, and a decision to be made. Perhaps to most of us, it just means we want time to think it over. But it means more than that, to creative people. It means more to my friend, M. F. Lees, a jeweler in Blind River, Ontario, which is near our Canadian retreat.

Every kind of watch problem comes to Lees, sooner or later, and some of them are tough ones He gets stumped at times, no matter what he does to try to fix the trouble in a watch. Does that bother him? Not at all. He sleeps on it. His preparation has been thorough: a long experience with many watch problems, and the effort put on this watch in particular. He confidently puts the pesky watch aside until the next day. In the meantime incubation takes over. Time and again, it has happened that he will awaken in the night, with the solution right there, as clear as can be. Or the inspiration may come next morning.

To me, this is a remarkable case of what might be called "habitual creativity."

ALTERNATION

Deliberate alternation is recognized as one of the important tricks to play in the creativity game. It is what Crane meant in that speech, in saying that we need "booster shots." Let's go back to the pocket knife example. Preparation includes holding the knife, toying with it, opening and shutting it, and working up an intense desire to improve it (Choice One). Then (Choice Two) you put it away, and largely out of mind, and let incubation proceed. Every day, perhaps, you return to preparation, with the knife present or even in hand; followed by incubation. This is alternation. These are booster shots. Sooner or later comes illumination, followed by the verification that comes from having a spring made that works, and modified until it works well.

Somewhere I have read of the system used by the great Cuvier, who did so much to classify and systematize fossils. In a large room he had fourteen tables, each with its own type of fossil. In the morning he would stop at the first table and try to get somewhere, fitting that one into the general scheme. Then on to the next. Day after day, he practiced alternation. May not this scheme have been considerably responsible for his amazing productivity?

PRESSURE

As described so far, the incubation period is pretty much free from any feeling of pressure to get the problem solved. But could it be that some pressure could serve to hasten illumination? My experience so indicates. As an experimenter and builder, I always have minor problems hanging around. Some demonstration item could be improved, and I hope to do it sometime. But how to do it in a nice, neat way has not come to mind. Then comes another time when I must make a trip with apparatus to give a lecture-demonstration. Apparatus must be packed.

Now, there is this about the packing job: It is not a chore. I get a lift from it. It means taking to the road again. I like to travel, and I love to give these demonstrations. This lift of the spirit, and the desire to give a good show may help account for what happens. I come to that item that still needs improvement. Yes, I am under pressure, for it takes time to pack, and time is limited. But the way to improve that item may now come, clear as can be. If the time can possibly be spared, I may whiz down to our shop for a bit of drilling, or perhaps some lathe work, and have the large satisfaction of having an item that works better or looks better. It has happened too many times to be ignored.

And don't miss the fact that there is a lot of alternation working for me in that process.

PRODUCTIVE PRESSURE FROM A DEADLINE

An extremely interesting practice based on much experience is described‡ by Chester M. Sinnett, a contributing editor to *Research/Development*. He treats of cases in which there is a deadline—a time set for solution or completion. Observe that he uses the word "pressure." "As the time runs out, the pressure builds up both consciously and subconsciously. With practice, one learns to depend more and more upon the combination to come through before the zero hour. Alertness is the order of the day. Apparently the subconscious does not believe in repeating anything, so one must be ready to accept and record its ideas as they appear—day or night. Never again will there occur exactly the same set of circumstances which triggered a given solution, so be ready to jot down enough of the idea or ideas that you can rebuild the solution later. For more than ten years, this approach has worked so well for me that I depend on it consistently. Sometimes I may become a little worried as the scheduled time approaches, but the result has always been much better than it would be if conventional practices had been followed."

I have to think that Sinnett's contribution is of much importance. Instead of waiting indefinitely for the subconscious to report with the illumination, Sinnett puts a time limit on it!

Personally, I have had to meet deadlines by the thousands. Not thousands, of course, in instances of creativity leading to inventions; but in leading a busy and varied life: meeting class deadlines; deadlines for writing technical papers; deadlines for readying speeches; deadlines for preparing ordinances for consideration by the City Council—such experiences have verified Sinnett's practice, in their own ways. The preparation phase has been carried out, but it often leaves the mind in what seems to be a state of confusion. There is a feeling of disorganization, of unreadiness. Will

‡ "The Challenge of Personal Professional Development" (*Research/Development*, April 1967), p. 24.

this stuff ever get organized in time? Then, next day, or maybe that evening, and often shortly before the deadline, everything seems to fall into place.

Did you ever try this? I suggest you try it in writing your next theme or term paper. It works!

THE GREATEST DISCOVERY OF OUR CENTURY

Any worker in the life sciences would name at once the greatest discovery of this century; and many scientists in other areas would agree. It would be the discovery in 1953 of the structure of DNA. The fundamental chemical of which our genes are made is deoxyribonucleic acid, or DNA for short. What was its structure, and how could it be self-copying, to operate as the chemical basis of heredity? That was the problem.

The full story has been most delightfully told by one of the Nobel Prize winners, James D. Watson. Appearing first in *The Atlantic Monthly*, it is now in book* form. As far as I know, the path from initial urge to final success was one of the most unpredictable and chaotic that has happened in the history of science. You can appreciate this only by reading the full story. The way was filled with hunches, true and false. It hinged in part on data from the laboratory, in chemistry and X-ray diffraction. It demanded mathematical analysis at certain stages. It was filled with cut-and-try. It called for getting the hands into the act, to build trial models of the molecule. Alternation took place, time and time again. It was spotted with periods of intense work, followed by periods of equally complete relaxation.

Any manager of R & D effort who naïvely thinks his research teams should always go quickly and directly through the   preparation-incubation-illumination-verification   steps, to the successes he wants, should learn a lesson from this story.

Every creative person should read and enjoy Watson's book.

* James D. Watson, *The Double Helix—The Discovery of the Structure of DNA.* (New York: Atheneum Publishers, 1968).

ELEVEN

Memory

In the next chapter we will try to take a look at how the mind operates in the creative process. Before we get into that, however, the *memory* function of the brain needs discussion.

Your memory storage will never run short of "space." You have somewhere between ten and twenty *billion* neurons or nerve cells in that brain of yours. These are surrounded by tinier cells called glial cells. Recently, a Swedish expert has said that there are a hundred billion of these; furthermore, that any one of the billions of neurons may have ten thousand synaptic knobs, for interconnection with other neurons. As far as is known, all these cells will serve for the longest lifetime devoted to the most intensive learning.

Just *how* the brain stores a memory is unknown. It is one of the great puzzles facing man. Many workers are busy trying to throw a little light on the tremendous capacity of the brain to store information, and how it does it.

It is now established that we have a short-term memory and a long-term memory.

THE SHORT-TERM MEMORY

Very little thought is required to decide that we must have a short-term memory. Not may have, or should have, but must have. We receive millions of impressions, or stimuli, every day. If we automatically stored all of those in a permanent memory, even twenty billion neurons might be insufficient.

As I sit here typing and sometimes glancing out into the Canadian bush, I see rough ground, rocks, bushes, trees. I have looked at this scene thousands of times. But if you ask me to turn my back on it and make a rough sketch of just the *main* objects—the bigger rocks, the larger humps, the taller trees—I would largely fail. I have not needed that information. The next time I go that way, I will again do it with eyes open, I pick a path, I get there. On the way, some objects will get my *temporary* attention: a bright leaf, a bush with berries on it. Some of these will be stored in my short-term memory. That is temporary learning. Temporary learning does occur, but nearly all of it evaporates.

Suppose you send me on that little trip. I get around rocks and bushes and trees and am on my way. Then you call, and have me come back. I'll come back more readily and easily, in finding a path that "works." My short-term memory was busy, and for a brief interval, it can be drawn on to help me return the easy way.

The whole business of being alive and getting around, dodging people on the sidewalk, getting through doors, going down steps, driving along a highway, eating dinner, demands our having a short-term memory that will serve *briefly* if needed. But there is also the necessity that this infinity of pieces of information be not stored in the permanent memory. Whether research will ever fully reveal its nature neurologically, chemically, and functionally, is an open question.

It may be that when learning becomes fixed in the memory, it does so on a molecular basis, by way of protein synthesis. You may wish to look up the article* by Bernard W. Agranoff. When he injects a substance that blocks protein synthesis into the skull of a goldfish, and does it soon after the fish is trained to perform a simple task, it forgets that which it was taught.

* "Memory and Protein Synthesis" (*Scientific American,* June 1967), pp. 115–22.

THE RISK IN HAVING A SHORT-TERM MEMORY

The risk is simple to understand. If some information will be needed later, perhaps years later, and it gets only as far as to be put into the temporary or short-term memory, it won't be there. To say, "I forgot" is out of order. How can you forget something that wasn't learned in the first place?

In studying, it is very easy to mistake temporary learning for the real thing. Many a dropout from school or college has fallen into this trap. Say you are studying physics. There is a picture of a lab table with several items on it, connected in certain ways. You come to it the first time and give it a look. Several times in the study period, you look at it again. Have you learned it? In some degree, yes. Now we test you. We show you several pictures of lab tables, somewhat similarly fixed up. You reject them all. Then we show you one identical with that in the book, and at once you recognize it. So then, you must have learned it? Hold on. We test you again: take this pencil and this blank sheet of paper, and sketch the main features of the apparatus. If you fail, then we put it this way: you did learn well enough for *recognition,* but not well enough for *recall.* Too much got only into the short-term memory; and one or two items were so vaguely seen that they never even got that far.

One of your lines of interest shows up in an item in *Science News.* You read it, and say, "I must remember that!"—and then pass to other reading. Will you remember it? Very poorly, if at all. But if you come wide awake; read it again; note the page number and the date; perhaps mark it; perhaps get your hands into the act by making a note about it (even if you throw the note away)—you will have that item stowed away in your long-term memory.

Years ago, one of my graduates, Hank Morton, was Electrical Superintendent for the City of Pontiac. He had charge of the lighting system, the traffic signal system, and the fire-alarm system. He got to worrying about whether the average citizen would know where the nearest fire-alarm box was, in case of fire. He went to the editor of the local paper, and proposed an educational campaign. The editor turned him down, saying, "Everyone knows where the alarm boxes are."

That made Hank stubborn. First, he knew that there was an alarm box very close to the newspaper building. Second, he quietly made a survey of the sixty-three people employed in that building. *Not one of them knew that box was there!* In making their daily rounds, they had passed that box any number of times, *almost always without even observing it*. Whenever it did happen to be recognized in some glance, it only got into the short-term memory, and was lost.

THE LONG-TERM MEMORY

To store an item in the long-term memory, you need to give it attention and interest. But also, you must give it time. Recent research tells that a time lapse is needed, during which the information is somehow processed. Perhaps it first goes into the short-term memory, and then is passed into the long-term memory. Or perhaps there is a separate pathway. If memory occurs at the molecular level, and definitely proves related to protein synthesis, that may account for requiring some time for the processing. In any case, some time is needed. Thus, after an item is *apparently* learned, if the attention too soon passes to something else, the first item is stored only in fragmentary form, if at all.

This may account for the success of the tricks we have for acquiring permanent learning: reading it twice; making notes about it; underlining it; reading it aloud; and so on. Each may have its own peculiar value, and I suspect it does; but over all rides the fact that *time* is given to it—the time needed by the nervous system to process that item and get it into permanent storage. Relearning it by later reviews all the more gets it firmly implanted.

Of course, all through this chapter, we are dealing with factors vital to the total field of efficient learning, be it in school or out of it. And within that total field, we are of course concerned with creativity. How? Why, by acquiring, all along the way, a very large and varied background knowledge of things, properties, materials, processes, functions, effects, principles, laws, names of manufacturers, names of authorities in science and other areas—add your own examples. Sometime, somewhere, you will have a pressing need to be at least *aware* that you learned something; and if you cannot recall more than that at the time, you can look it up. Without that awareness, you won't even know of its existence.

DO WE EVER FORGET ANYTHING?

Astounding as it may seem, authorities are swinging to the belief that once something is stored in the long-term memory, it stays there and is never forgotten. The fact that you cannot recall, at will, the details of a happening, or even the happening itself, does not mean that it is gone. It is still in storage, but unused for so long that you cannot bring it back just by trying.

Wilder Penfield, the great brain surgeon of McGill University, has done more than anyone else to open up this kind of research. Once, he was ready to operate on the brain of a patient who was fully conscious (only local anesthetic is needed—the brain does not feel pain). He happened to touch an electrode to a certain exposed spot on the brain. At once, the patient began recalling a long-gone happening, in remarkable detail. It came in proper sequence. As it unfolded, the patient declared that it was actually happening right there in the surgery, even though aware of the realities of the present at the same time. Later, when the same spot was stimulated, the "record played itself over again."

We also have the evidence from hypnosis, by which a subject is enabled to recall a childhood event, or a movie long since seen. Such findings strongly indicate that the long-term memory hangs onto everything that gets into it.

INACTIVE STORAGE

In this chapter we have seen, first, that we have a short-term or temporary memory, for what we might call moment-to-moment living. We have seen, second, that we have a long-term memory of tremendous capacity. And now for a third kind of thing: nearly everything stored in the long-term memory gets into a state that I choose to call "inactive storage." It is there all right, but so long unused that little of it can be brought out, no matter how hard you try. That very large amount of learned material that we do keep available and always ready for use is so kept, by use and reuse; but the vastly greater amount *must* be tucked away somehow, in ordinary inaccessible form.

Why can we say this? Because the mind has, and must have, the ability to associate. One recalled item, somehow associated with a second item, "reminds us," as we say, of the second. The second could remind us of two or three more. If we had complete and automatic recall of everything we "know" (everything stored), the recall of a single item would pull the cork. An endless, tangled flood of remembered material would overwhelm us. If this happened, and we had no way to shut it off, we would be totally useless. We think of salt. That starts it. Thinking of salt brings out the taste of it. That brings out the taste of sugar, weak acid, pickles; from pickles to cucumbers to potatoes to potato bugs—there we go, hopelessly victimized by a perfect and complete memory of enormous proportions, insistent on being poured out. What a horrifying thought!

Yes, but this leads to an ominous thought. You learn some information today. Two decades pass. You have not needed, not used it. It has moved into inactive storage. It is not accessible to a conscious recall effort. And then—that is the very item you *must* have, to round out the invention you are working on. Are you helpless? No! The next chapter deals with that.

MANAGING THE MIND

That word "mind"—what is the mind? This question has raged in controversy. I gladly avoid controversy by saying very little here about it.

I think of the mind as the functioning of the brain-body

organism. If that functioning is impaired, the mind is impaired. Drugs, anesthetics, and so on, can temporarily impair or derail the nervous system, and the person has temporarily "lost his mind."

Notice that instead of speaking of the functioning of the brain only, I spoke of the *brain-body* organism. You cannot separate the two. We do not need drugs to throw the mind out of gear. Recent research has shown that if a man is isolated practically completely from incoming stimuli, so that he feels nothing, sees nothing, tastes nothing, hears nothing, smells nothing, he soon cannot think: He hallucinates. The effective functioning of the mind requires the functioning of the whole organism.

In the creative process, how can the mind best be managed? And in particular, what is it doing in that mysterious incubation period, coming after preparation, and leading to illumination?

TWELVE

The Mind: Conscious and Subconscious

If you wish to spend the rest of your life on "the problem of the mind," you certainly can. There will be plenty of room for you. And you will live in controversy. At one extreme, some psychiatrists are almost mystic, ascribing to the mind qualities hardly to be explained by nerve tracts alone. At another extreme we have neuroanatomists—looking at nerve pathways, synapses, sensory and motor tracts, feedback provisions, and so on—and having little respect for psychiatrists. Somewhat in between there are hardboiled psychologists, who think that microanatomy is good because it gives the neurologists something to do, and that psychiatry isn't a science at all: that what really matters is to observe the whole person under different conditions to see how he responds; devise tests, mental and experimental; and accept no hypothesis until it stands up under test.

If you join the psychologists, you will not avoid differences in viewpoints and beliefs. Psychologists favor our having different phases or "levels" of mind operation, but they look at these things in different ways. You find them using terms such as conscious, preconscious, unconscious, subconscious. Those writing about creativity use additional terms, such as divergent thinking, convergent thinking, and others.

Webster's defines both *unconscious* and *subconscious*. Writers on creativity differ: Some use one term, some the other. I tend to think that the psychiatrist delves into the unconscious, but that the creative individual makes use of the subconscious. Certainly some will not like this description of our mind levels.

All that any one writer can do is this: After reading widely, he will present his own interpretation—inevitably tempered, of course, by his own feelings and his own experience. That's the way it is here.

THE CONSCIOUS

With your conscious mind, you are aware. You know what's going on. Let us walk from our cabin to the beach. You see a smooth stone, water-worn and rounded. You pick it up. Heavy. You knew it would be. You toss it out over the lake. You knew it would make that curve. There is a splash. You expected it. The waves make a widening circle. You knew they would. No surprises, no problems.

Now, you pick up a tiny pebble and toss it straight up. There is a wind, and it falls to one side. Why not? It occurs to you that if you could standardize your pebbles, and the upward velocity, the sidewise drift would serve to measure wind velocity. Correct. You have just invented a wind gauge!

The foregoing brought the conscious mind into play. Your experience (your stored memories) told you all that was going to happen. All but one: It didn't predict the invention of that wind gauge. You used the scientific method in reasoning from cause to effect, when the wind (the cause) made the sidewise drift (the effect). But you went far beyond that, in being a creative person who could, on the spot, come up with a use for that effect. Most people would never have made that invention at all. Every element of the invention was so very familiar that we are tempted to say that it was forced to happen. Not so. For most people, the conscious effort would have stopped with merely noting a familiar sidewise drift of the pebble.

The conscious mind is logical. It reasons from cause to effect. In the rare instance, as in this one, a conscious chain of reasoning may lead you immediately to make the discovery or invention. But it is rare, even for the most creative individuals; and the noncreative never get there at all.

THE SUBCONSCIOUS

We now come to the central mystery of the creative process. The subconscious mind has been described as a workhorse that will blindly follow your orders, perform fantastic labors for you without your knowing it, and then hand you the vitally needed illumination without ever revealing how it arrived at it. Whether you call it the subconscious or the unconscious makes no difference. In the course of time, both terms may be dropped, in favor of new names.

The fact that we know next to nothing about it cannot be allowed to let us walk away from the subject and ignore it. Why? Because we cannot ignore the actual experiences of creative people. We have to account for those experiences in some way.

Let us take a simple example. While at the beach, I ask you what we are standing on. You tell me: sand. Then I remind you that ordinary glass is 70 per cent sand, plus soda ash, plus lime. Yes, but what *kind* of sand?

Now, you "know" the answer, and you are sure that you "know" it. But if my luck is good, I have trapped you. The word "silica" is in your memory storage, but is not immediately accessible. As you have found from many such experiences, the harder you try (consciously) to order your mind to produce that word, the less you succeed. But you also know that if we drop the subject, "silica" will unexpectedly pop into your conscious mind in five minutes, or tonight, or maybe next week.

In this case, the subconscious (or whatever it is) apparently went on a memory search. In creative work, it can do far more: It can lead to illumination.

THE SUBCONSCIOUS GOES TO WORK

Again, at this point, we call on that speech by Crane, and take his summary of what Poincaré said: "Poincaré goes on to point out that we would get nowhere by simply trying, consciously, to make all possible combinations of all the pieces of information in our heads. The number of combinations would be too vast; the job of sorting the promising ones from the nonsensical ones would require more than a lifetime, even for the solving of a simple problem. . . . Once the brain has come seriously to grips with the problem, it works through the millions of combinations and possibilities, assesses them, and discards most of them, *unconsciously.* . . . The process continues, during both waking and sleeping hours, even simultaneously with the person's conscious activities. . . . The winning idea, when it is found, may pop into the consciousness at any time. . . . It may happen right in the middle of some entirely different activity."

A friend, Prof. Joseph Datsko, tells me of a recent experience. For months, he repeatedly tried to make sense of certain data concerning the bending of metal sheets. He intuitively felt that a valuable correlation would come, if only the right way to plot the data could be found. No success came. Then at home one night, he was doing *two* things at once: talking with his wife, and watching a TV program. In the midst of that, he said right out loud, "I've got it!" And he had, too.

How does the subconscious ceaselessly do this memory searching (even into the inactive storage), and sorting and testing, and finally come up with the illumination? We do not know. We may never know. But these things happen, and they happen during incubation.

ILLUMINATION ON THE LACKAWANNA FERRY

By 1927, the vacuum tube had been born. Its ability to amplify had already found many uses. But it somewhat distorted the signal. It was known that if only that distortion could be eliminated, the long-distance telephone, by land and by submarine cable, could be extended indefinitely by using repeater stations.

Harold S. Black had been working on this problem for several years, but was getting nowhere. One morning, going again to work at Bell Laboratories, he took the Lackawanna

Ferry. He sat down. Illumination came, then and there, in terms of the invention of negative feedback. He thus tamed the vacuum tube and gave the world a concept of such basic importance and so indispensable in so great a number of uses, that its value is almost beyond any figure we could place on it.

But, more to that ferry ride. *That* was the morning when, by error, Black's morning paper had a whole blank page in it. He settled right down, used the page, drew the circuit, and wrote the equation for performance!

THE SUBCONSCIOUS TAKES INVENTORY

I had a startling experience in March 1964. I was starting on my western tour of sixteen colleges and universities, to give lecture-demonstrations. In packing the apparatus for that ten-thousand-mile jaunt, I had to be sure to take dozens of items. The first stop was at a motel in Chicago. I went to bed. At 4 A.M. I came wide awake, and an inner voice seemed to say, "Did I bring the ring!" An inspection that day showed that a brass ring, used in a demonstration, was the one thing I had forgotten!

THE TEAM: CONSCIOUS AND SUBCONSCIOUS

For creative work we have, then, a wondrously competent team, each member of which is indispensable in its own way, but each helpless without the other.

The conscious mind is logical. We reason with it. With it we recognize a problem. With it we get ideas about how to attack the problem. With it we dream up hypotheses, and lines of attack for testing them. With it we design our apparatus, lay out our experiments, and decide what data to collect. With it we do a lot of hard, conscientious, conscious work. But typically, the discovery or invention does not come through. (In fact, hypotheses arising in the conscious mind may be wrong; the right one may come later from the subconscious.)

Was all that hard work necessary? Yes. Of course, this

preparation phase can vary enormously. Depending partly on luck, partly on ability to plan (and, no doubt, on other factors), a lot of unnecessary work may, on later review, be seen to have been done. But the work must be done for two reasons. First, new learning essential to solving the problem must be acquired. Second, all the time the hard work goes on, we are ordering our subconscious mind to get busy. It seems we are placing that order, whether we know it or not.

Furthermore, those who know how to play this game *know* that they are placing the order to the subconscious to get on with the job. Being confident that it can do so seems all the more to guarantee success.

THE TEAM AT WORK

Here then, in brief, is the team at work:

PREPARATION: conscious effort (meanwhile ordering the subconscious to get busy).

INCUBATION: the subconscious takes over, searches the memory bank, hunts for the right combination.

ILLUMINATION: the subconscious reports to the conscious.

VERIFICATION: conscious effort, to verify that the right problem was solved; and if so, that the illumination was not faulty.

THIRTEEN

On Various Matters

This is an odds-and-ends chapter, where discussions that can more or less stand on their own feet are gathered together. Among other things, it will dare to consider that provocative question: Are women creative?

ARE WOMEN CREATIVE?

Yes, women are creative. A good many women have become great novelists, playwrights, and artists. Women have made important discoveries in astronomy, physics, medicine, biology, and like areas. I suspect that the number of these discoveries is on the increase.

But the history of discovery and invention is overwhelmingly a history of *men* and what they did. Could it be solely a matter of greater opportunity for men, and lack of it for women? After all, only recently did women earn the right to vote. Until then, in our Western culture, it was held that woman's place was in the home; and the home offers little chance to make scientific discoveries or technological inventions. Now that women are emanicapted, and more and more are finding their way into shops, laboratories, and offices, it could be argued that by the year 2000, women will equal men in creativity in most fields of endeavor. But will the opportunity be there?

Women, on the whole, cannot give up child-rearing and home maintenance, and cannot give up child-bearing at all. Men, on the whole, cannot give up working and supporting families. These simple facts of life will continue to deny equal opportunity to a large fraction of women.

Comes the next question: Are women *potentially* equal to men in creativity? Here, my own thoughts have to turn to evolution. Speaking of preman, the family group had to survive. Somebody had to go out to hunt, and be able to fight predators or other tribes. The males, larger and stronger, had to do it. The females had to bear and keep the young, and do the "at-home" chores. Much the same thing prevailed in the immensely long period of the evolutionary development of man himself.

Evolution inevitably selects in favor of those qualities that enable a species to survive. This called for men who could go out to fight, to compete, to pioneer. It called for women who could raise the family and take care of the home. Evolution proceeded in its inexorable way, and we are its products. You are quite free to draw your own conclusions. My conclusion is that we must expect considerable differences between most men and most women as to viewpoints, interests, and abilities; and therefore, differences in areas in which creativity may occur. Each sex may be potentially superior to the other, depending on which area of creativity is investigated.

It has been suggested that women have a "people orientation," while men have an "object orientation." To me, there seems to be a lot of truth in this. And, of course, if true, it is largely or perhaps wholly a matter of evolution for the survival of the species. For our purposes here, I would prefer to think of what may be much the same thing, but in somewhat different terms: that most men are occupation-centered, and most women are home-centered.

This leads me to propose an idea that may be new in the literature on creativity. From my general reading, I have the strong impression that many, perhaps most of the scientific advances made by women, come from women in laboratories. I wish to propose that for a woman, the laboratory serves as an extension of the home. I speak now not of women serving as technicians, but of the professionals—some of the 11 per cent who take the Ph.D. degree. In the laboratory, as in the home, there are complex processes to be carried out, with a variety of materials and processes to be manipulated. Often, as in the home, there are skilled hand-and-finger operations to perform. In the home, the woman has her family. In the laboratory she again has her "family," the research team. It seems to me that there are too many parallels here to be ignored, and that some research ought to be done on it. Often she is the only woman on the team, and with the incentive to show that she is just as good as any man, if not better.

If I had a creative daughter looking for a career, I would not hesitate to argue as above, and perhaps get her to look into some such environment as is offered in a research laboratory.

LILY PAVEY AND THE MUSIKRITER

A woman's invention that delights me is now offered by a British firm. It is called the Musikriter. For centuries, composers have yearned for a faster and easier way to write music. Undoubtedly, many men have tackled the problem, and failed. Lily Pavey, who had only a year and a half of formal schooling, invented it. As told in *Time*, December 4, 1964, she is a former circus clown, and can play seventeen different musical instruments. (Remember the high creative adolescents who preferred unconventional occupations?)

While typing invoices at home to make a living, she took to singing to relieve the boredom. Came this thought: It would be more fun to type music, than invoices. She bought an old typewriter and spent years trying to modify it. The big breakthrough came from riding in an elevator: It led to her vertical typing scheme. And please note this: Lily Pavey made this invention right in her home, and did it by using her ingenuity to marry two skills she had in high degree: typing and musicianship.

DISCOVERERS AND INVENTORS

Is there a distinction between *discovery* and *invention?* There is. You don't invent a mountain; but if you are the first to see it, you have discovered it. The human body has a great many enzymes that operate as catalysts. Evolution has already "invented" them. Some day, as a biochemist, you may discover one not already known. If there is a medical need for it, and you develop a way to synthesize it, you have invented a process, and you can patent the process. You could not patent the enzyme, for you cannot patent a material found in nature.

It is often said that pure scientists are interested in discovering the facts and laws of nature; that for them, this is the end sought, and the discovery brings its own satisfactions. Applied scientists and engineers, on the other hand, take over from such discoveries, to produce useful things for the benefit of mankind. This is, of course, an extreme picture. There is much overlap. In either case, man's creativity is at work.

Furthermore, overlap can occur in the same man. A scientist, wishing to make a discovery, may have to invent the apparatus he needs to get on with the problem. An engineer, wishing to invent, may find that science has not caught up with his needs, and this may lead him to become a discoverer in order to proceed with the invention.

When Alfred Nobel wrote his last will in 1896 and in it provided for the award of Nobel prizes, he obviously tried to take such distinctions into account. He said that the physics prize would be for the most important discovery or invention; the chemistry award for discovery or improvement; and in physiology or medicine, for discovery. He did not define any of the three terms.

THE CREATIVE ENVIRONMENT

Perhaps the world's greatest industrial research complex is Bell Telephone Laboratories. Bell research used to be centered in a building in New York, and I used to visit it in those days. Then came the giant laboratories at Murray Hill, New Jersey. I have lectured there, and have had the privilege of seeing one of the finest research layouts in the world. It has served as a model for many others. M. J. Kelly, now retired, ably directed it for many years. He, and my former student, Jack Morton, vice president, have kindly described for me their concept of a good creative environment in a research complex. It is this: Give the research man a laboratory with all facilities, and space needed for his work; but *nearby*, also give him a cubicle—a little office to which he retreats. Murray Hill is so laid out. The researcher shuttles between two worlds. In the laboratory he directs his technicians and his team, if any; makes measurements and observations, tests out new apparatus or devices. In his cubicle he can do his heavy thinking, make computations, design apparatus, write reports; or, on occasion, just stare into space. If he needs more mathematics than he can handle, no worry: plenty of mathematicians are on call; he may have one on his team. The great success of the Laboratories must in part hinge on the admirable facilities.

But that isn't all. The best facilities can never make up for a lack of good relationships. We are speaking of mental and emotional factors. Here again, the Laboratories are a shining example of maintaining a favorable "creative climate."

In this regard, a notable finding came from a study made at another large industrial research enterprise, Arthur D. Little, Inc. The study was *intended* to find what physical facilities were most favorable to research productivity. What really came out of it was that providing the best facilities is less important than having the right attitudes around the place. Do the workers respect each other? Are there good team leaders? Are the research directors respected, and effective?

In a firm, there can be a problem of convincing the management that a discovery or invention should be taken up, developed, and produced for the market. Management can range from being aggressive to ultraconservative. Managers, perhaps excellent in other respects, may not be creative; and, to protect their own records, may find it much easier to say no to a new thing. There is nothing speculative about this statement: Able consultants to management have too often found it so. This is a serious problem, especially in large firms where there may be several layers of supervision and management to convince before there can be a recommendation to the top to go ahead. Thus, while the creative environment for the inventor or the research team, at his or its level, may be fine, there can be the discouraging feeling that, after all, this new thing may have a poor chance of being adopted up above. Keep this in mind when reading about the employed inventor in the next chapter.

Anyone in any capacity who is responsible for bringing out creativity among those working for him should never forget that a creative person needs encouragement at the outset of his project, interest and support while furthering it, and adequate recognition at its successful conclusion, whether or not it becomes commercially profitable.

FACTORS AFFECTING CREATIVITY

"Necessity is the mother of invention." An old saying. Now reverse it, and get, "Invention is the mother of necessity." True also in many cases. In earlier days, a common impression of the inventor was of a man starving in an attic, struggling against great odds to perfect his invention. That was no myth. It happened.

If you read Mitchell Wilson's fine book, you will learn how some great American inventors did work against those odds—driven to dire necessity pursuing the goal; and after achieving inventive success, how some fatefully lost the battle to forces greater than themselves. Some died discouraged and defeated. Samuel Morse escaped this, and died wealthy and revered; but think of how he gave up a lucrative career as a painter, and was actually near starvation before his telegraph brought success.

We hear much of "Yankee ingenuity." No doubt, most of us think that we became famed for that, almost from the beginning. The truth is otherwise, as Mitchell Wilson makes plain. There were American handicrafts; there had to be, with a continent to conquer. But for most it was a hard life, and in Colonial days craftsmanship was inferior. A man tended to be a jack-of-all-trades, and not really skilled at any. Workmanship, except for such things as silversmithing and clockmaking, was on the crude side. The colonials did exhibit energy and enterprise in using water power for gristmills and sawmills, and in shipbuilding, where carpenters, millwrights, and other artisans of handicrafts could furnish the necessary skills. But remember: English law prevailed. The colonies were required to feed raw materials to England, where the processing took place. Technology had no chance to be encouraged under these strictures.

Furthermore, winning our independence liberated men's minds politically, but not, at once, for innovation. America was broke. Times were hard. A foreign commerce had to be built up. Wilson says, "There were so few mechanics that when Robert Fulton . . . in 1805 . . . wanted to build one of his clockwork torpedoes . . . he could find only one mechanic in New York . . . who could follow his plans." Even that late in our history, an inventor was much more likely to be laughed at than encouraged. Thus, it was a good many years after the Revolution before Yankee ingenuity had a real chance to get started.

Throughout the long history of the human race, we find that creativity has nearly always had to struggle against anything from discouragement to violent rejection. Those who wish to review that history will surely want to read an excellent paper* by Eugene Ayres, an internationally known authority on sources of energy, of the Gulf Research and Development Corporation.

Today we no longer burn down the shop where an inventor is suspected of making something "that will throw men out of work." Instead, the inventor isn't in that little shop on a side street. He is often a well-paid scientist or engineer in a firm. Innovation is part of his job. If manage-

---

* "Social Attitude toward Invention" (*American Scientist*, Vol. 43, No. 4, October 1955), pp. 521–40.

ment is as it should be, he is given encouragement to get that new thing to a stage where the firm can put it into production and onto the market.

Less than half a century ago, Dr. Banting had a practice too small to support a family. He took a job to help out; and on a miserably small grant, got the dogs with which to experiment. From that came insulin. Today, the support for medical research is such that attics in which to starve are no longer available: there is no demand for them. Today, there is so much support for scientific research and so much waiting to be done that almost anyone with promise, and energy, can find a welcome and a way to make a living.

Thus, the climate for creativity has changed greatly for the better. With a reservation or two, however.

RESERVATIONS

An individual can become intensely motivated in seeking his goal. It is *his* goal. Can a research team likewise become keyed up and remain keyed up? Yes, it happens, but it might be the exception rather than the rule.

The cost of R & D (research and development) has steadily mounted, to where viewers of the scene are worried about it. Research team efficiency is being called into question. The National Science Foundation has found that the publication items per scientist or engineer is steadily rising, while the patents taken out per man are steadily falling. This could represent a huge waste of money and talent. Thus, one reservation about a bulky section of modern creative endeavor has been stated.

I am impelled to mention another. In many cases, is it too easy for the individual to get on the research team? True, the graduate has worked pretty hard to get into college, through college, and to get that Ph.D. But today, he may go through college on scholarships; in the graduate school, grants support him and his research needs. When ready for the "market," he can often choose from among a number of excellent offers. How well is he economically motivated, compared with those of a generation ago, many of whom partly earned their way, and then had to look lively to find a job? Can you wonder that too often, he has the feeling that he "has it made"? A feeling of "having it made" is not a very good guarantee of giving dedicated service in a research team.

All of which leaves the door to opportunity wide open to you, if you realize the significance of these factors in advance. If you join a team, give it your best. If you do, you may be promoted even before you expect to be!

A word about specialization: Specialize if you must, but keep your eyes and mind open to a wide array of interests. The company you join cannot know what it will be doing in ten years. The same goes for you.

BRAINSTORMING

"Brainstorming" is the name given to a group session in which all discouragements and prejudgments are barred, and every member is urged to come up with ideas, no matter how wild. It has been used as a training technique, to improve the free-wheeling abilities of the members: getting them to turn loose from the conservative, the tried-and-true. The hope is that a habit of entertaining all kinds of hunches will carry over to when real problems are tackled. It has been tried to some extent in science and engineering.

There is literature on it. I have always had my doubts about it. Perhaps there is more to it than I think. With that, I will drop the subject.

A BASIC PATENT AND

ITS FAR-REACHING EFFECTS

Johnny Spencer, at fifteen, observed that clean-out door that popped (see Chapter Seven). He could not foresee what all that would lead to, but he never gave up trying to do something about it. He applied for his patent on the Spencer disc on April 8, 1921, and was granted Patent No. 1,448,240 on March 13, 1923. He formed the Spencer

Thermostat Company, and later took out over sixty more patents on the device.

The Westinghouse Electric Company (now Corporation) obtained an exclusive license for electrical applications in 1923, and had an active program for licensing other companies to use these discs. For twenty years or more, the discs were used in electric flatirons. But before this use could be made, another problem had to be solved. The early discs would operate only at more moderate temperatures. But L. K. Marshall, with the Spencer outfit, invented a higher-temperature bimetal combination (Patent No. 1,481,-021), and the flatiron application became possible.

As often happens, invention at the licensee (Westinghouse) was stimulated, and patents developed there. One, to H. S. Gano, was Patent No. 1,693,379, for the Thermoguard, to protect motors from overheating. Such devices now protect over one billion motors. The Bolesky Patent No. 2,199,388 added a manual reset button. Another important Westinghouse offshoot for using the discs in motor starters and circuit breakers to protect aircraft circuits, was covered in the Dorfman Patent No. 1,985,023. These uses have run into hundreds of thousands.

The Spencer Thermostat Company merged with the General Plate Company in 1930, to become the Metals & Controls Corporation. In turn, this corporation became a division of Texas Instruments, Inc. in 1954. This firm continues to make thermostats and controls in a wide variety of forms and sizes for a great many applications. Two offshoot companies also appeared: the Therm-O-Disc Company and the Stevens Manufacturing Company, both of Mansfield, Ohio.

And, to show just a bit of how men, devices, and firms can overlap in so many ways, we mention Gordon K. Teal again (see Chapter Eight), who did so much at Bell Telephone Laboratories to develop the basics for the solid-state industry: He is Assistant Vice President of Texas Instruments, of which Metals & Controls is a division. And Teal gives much credit to Jack Morton, vice president at Bell Telephone Laboratories, for giving him critically needed financial support and encouragement when he started his crystal growing.

QUESTION: *When a youngster of fifteen is around when an old clean-out door does something unexpected, should he pay any attention to it?*

SHOULD YOU KEEP A JOURNAL?

Yes. You should keep a journal. No matter how young you are, no matter how inexperienced, no matter how much you think you are not ready for serious creativity, keep a journal. In fact, in later years when you go back to your early notes, the more you see of "kid ideas" that didn't pan out, the more you will treasure them.

If you have never kept a journal, there is no time like right now for making a start. Get some kind of notebook. If you wish, your first entry could be, "Today, I read Chapter Thirteen in *Creativity,* and the man said I ought to keep a journal."

The orderliness with which creative people keep journals varies greatly. If your standards of neatness are unduly high, you may soon drop the journal habit: you just don't have time to make it neat, and you don't want to "spoil" those blank pages. The other extreme is to be so sloppy that even the world's best detectives and code-breakers could not make sense of the notations. Somewhere in between is where you should operate. As you mature, so will your ideas, and journal notations may become very important to you, for patent protection (see Appendix).

You might think that this little lecture comes from one who has religiously kept journals for at least half a century. The truth is that I am not a journalkeeper. I spend very little time regretting the past, but I confess that this is a major regret. *Please* don't be like me. *Keep a journal!* Of course, I have many thick folders on file of research notes, studies, designs, and so on. But a journal would have strung these together; it would have recorded things I have forgotten; and it could tell me now of many a visitor and friend who dropped in. Keep a journal!

FOURTEEN

The Independent and the Captive Inventor

In earlier days, the independent inventor was "it." In that simpler technology, firms did not make it a business to originate. If an independent inventor created something a firm wanted, it made a deal with him. With the increasingly complex nature of science and technology, firms have found it essential to set up their own research and development departments. Out of these come inventions that are patented. Thus a firm protects its position in a changing world, and does what it can to promote its standing and the market for its products. Thus, there are many employed inventors, or "captive" inventors.

THE INDEPENDENT INVENTOR

In this regulated life we lead, it is always refreshing to find an activity one can pursue without taking courses, passing tests, paying fees, and getting a license to practice. The inventor is still free to start in without notifying the government that he is about to build better mousetraps. I find this a comforting idea.

The independent inventor is on his own. It is entirely up to him what he will work at, when he will work at it, and how hard he will work at it. All of which sounds fine until we ask how he makes a living. Well, that varies much, from one man to another. A man already wealthy does not have that problem; but then, very seldom does he have the urge to be creative. A rare exception was George Ellery Hale, with a wealthy father and inherited wealth. His consuming interest in astronomy was given complete support by his father. As you know, it was his ingenuity, his great interest in the sun, his ability to organize, and his way of coaxing large gifts from rich men, that brought us the two-hundred-inch telescope. A *very* exceptional case.

There is the rather rare inventor who lives on income from previous inventions. Leo H. Baekeland comes to mind, a brilliant young Belgian professor (and friend of Michael Pupin), who came to this country. He invented Velox, the first photographic paper that would print by artificial light. After George Eastman, of Eastman Kodak, paid him one million dollars for the rights to Velox, Baekeland could go his own way as an independent inventor. And from him came that great contribution, Bakelite. Success breeds success. A man in that position is in fine shape to keep on being productive.

Very different is the man who would starve, if not working at something else while inventing. Invention then must be a spare-time activity. Chester F. Carlson, beginning in 1937, had an idea for using electrostatics for making copies. His first results were pretty dismal, but he hung on. He had many reverses and discouragements. Seventeen companies had a chance to take on his idea and develop it. They all turned him down. They all now spend part of their time regretting it. In 1944, Carlson arranged for Battelle Memorial Institute to develop the process; and there, Walkup had a great deal to do with the successful battle to bring it through. Finally, it came out as Xerox, which promptly effected a tremendous revolution in the copying field. And Carlson? He is a very wealthy man.

Whatever the circumstances, the lone inventor is putting time and effort and money into his brainchild, before any money comes out of it. Sometimes he finds a backer; otherwise, it is his money. It takes faith, stamina, and strong motivation to keep this up for very long. It can be a tough row to hoe.

Also, there is ample reason to be concerned about what lies beyond making the invention—if it does come through. Is it patentable? It may be a fine invention, but turn out to be a reinvention (already old; or if new, some other inventor may already have filed a patent application). If a patent is obtained, can the inventor make and market it himself? Or can he interest a company? If either happens, will it be a commercial success? If it is, will someone bring a patent suit and take the patent to court? This costs plenty, and the court might invalidate the patent. All this is not in the least intended to discourage the independent inventor, but to make sure he enters the game with open eyes.

Years ago, an inventor friend of mine was washed out by still another factor. In those days, the auto was a simple contraption for getting you from one place to another. It still had far to go to be fancied up. It needed a windshield defroster. He invented one, and somewhere in my lab I still have the one he gave me. You stuck it against the inside of the windshield by means of two rubber vacuum cups. The cups held a little steel bar. A little reflector was mounted on the bar, with a coiled resistance wire in the reflector heated by battery current. After the heat cleared a spot, you moved the reflector along, and soon, you widened the spot to a band, to make a wide peephole. My friend made a deal with a nearby company, and the defroster went to market. It lost money the first year. The second year, the same story. But the third year coming up looked rosy: sales of fifty thousand were expected. And? Well, some creative chaps elsewhere had been busy, perfecting safety glass for windshields; it took over; and safety glass does not take kindly to localized heating. The invention came off the windshield. Made obsolete!

The way of the independent inventor can be rough indeed, and sometimes is. It takes faith in one's ability to keep at it and carry through. It calls for a degree of incurable optimism. It needs the balancing effect of enough sanity to forget disappointment if the worst happens, and to pick up the pieces and carry on to a fresh start on the next idea. You can't win them all, you know. I greatly admire the independent inventor, and wish we had more of him.

There are some who write as if things are closing in on the independent, to squeeze him out. One writer, in a highly responsible post, argues that discoveries occur out at the frontiers of our knowledge; that science is already so extensive and complex that much knowledge has to be mastered before a man can even *get* to the frontier—and therefore, he has to get there by the Ph.D. route. He concludes that we must train as many as possible by way of the doctorate. As far as this goes he speaks much truth, and much of it would apply to the independent inventor who *does* want to get out there on the frontier's fringes. But in my candid opinion, that writer doesn't see the woods for the trees. I insist on believing that there is still, and always will be, a large field of invention right back at home, so to speak, in areas served by inventors who work at things calling for high ingenuity, rather than long training that comes from spending years on a campus learning what others already know.

Another encouragement comes from viewing the giant corporations. With their fine research teams, they do their best to make all the inventions they need. They try, but never can do it all. Time and again, the discovery or invention a corporation needs, or can use in a profitable line of goods, doesn't originate inside. It may occur in another firm. Often it comes from an independent inventor. Estimates from a few giants indicate that a half or more of their profits are based on outside inventions which they buy, or on which they pay royalties.

The *amateur* independent inventor does need some guidance. In a small way, turn professional as fast as possible. Read widely. Read invention case histories. Be acutely aware that your "new" idea may be old. Learn about patents. Learn what a patent search is. Learn what "evidence of conception" is. (Some of these matters are mentioned briefly in the Appendix.) Talk with experts, other inventors, and patent attorneys at every opportunity. And learn this, once and forevermore: *Ethical patent attorneys do not advertise loudly.*

Here is a hopeful fact: We have lots of independent inventors, as the Appendix makes plain.

THE EMPLOYED, OR CAPTIVE, INVENTOR

Compared to the independent inventor, the employed inventor works under very different circumstances. Variations in the terms of employment cannot be discussed here, so I will pass to the most usual situation. The man is not directly hired to be an inventor. There are all kinds of titles within a company, but you look in vain for a door with anything like this on it: John Doe, Inventor. A firm takes a man because it needs that kind of man. Young college graduates may be hired in numbers, to be sorted out gradually by interests and abilities. Older men may be hired from other firms for filling in where special training and competence are needed.

If that sounds as if the firm is not much interested in invention, the truth is quite the opposite. It is vitally interested, and in this competitive world it has to be. Out of these acquisitions of manpower must eventually come some of the developments that help to keep the firm competitive, alive, and able to make a profit. If it fails to make a profit over too long a period, it goes out of business, and many people suffer. Therefore, it must look upon every new scientist or engineer hired, as a potential inventor; and, as an inventor, not for himself, but for the company.

Therefore, typically, the new employee is asked to sign an agreement. If he invents, he will help in every way to patent the invention; the patent will issue in his name; he will then assign the patent to the firm. He is, in effect, a captive inventor.

When they first learn about this state of affairs, some young people in high school, and some in college tend to rebel. The usual reaction is, "I don't like this at all; if I make an invention, it ought to be mine!" Let's see about that. In the great majority of cases, the firm already has a large stake in the invention. The idea for it comes while working for the company, and on account of work going on there. Much of the knowledge leading to the idea is learned while in the firm. The firm allows time for working it up, and may assign expensive equipment and apparatus to further the effort. After all that, what right does the inventor have to say, "That's mine!" The firm must survive. It has every right, as long since backed by court decisions, to expect its employees to work, and to invent, for *it*. If instead, it furnished every facility for making an invention, and then permitted the inventor to leave with his patent and go to a rival firm, how long would it stay in business?

Ethically, an employed inventor will not resign, taking with him his quietly perfected invention, and peddle it elsewhere.

Legally, court decisions have required such an invention to be returned to the company of origin, depending on how much time has elapsed. It seems to be up to the court to decide on "how much" time.

A young fellow may still want to know if he will be rewarded when his patent is taken over. At the time of takeover, there may be a payment of one dollar, as "legal consideration." Firms vary widely as to making any immediate award over and above that. There is no fixed scheme. As to later reward, there is, and has to be, a wait-and-see attitude. Why? A patent may never benefit the company, for many patents never have commercial value. Or again, the invention may be an improvement on an invention patented by someone else; if that patent owner is not interested in the improvement, there is no way to make him use it. Or a patent that looks like a world-beater today can be scrapped tomorrow by some development that makes it obsolete. No man can read the future in these respects.

Thus, there is no way whatever to precisely evaluate a patent in advance; or often, for years later. It commonly takes from two to fifteen years for a firm to start making a profit from an invention. The technological development may take time: or the public may just not be ready to accept the product. Also, very large sums can be spent on development, only to find that some insurmountable obstacle remains insurmountable. If the product does reach the market, patent suits may arise that can be costly indeed. These are real risks the firm must face, and the inventor has to recognize them. Therefore, the inventor's reward most often comes as further encouragement to invent, added responsibility, and promotion to higher rank and pay.

Of course, a great many creative men are only too glad to fit themselves into the employee-inventor ranks. The firm takes all the risks. Its large resources can supply them with laboratories, equipment, supplies, apparatus, technicians, and such. Many discoveries and inventions cannot be made unless these advantages are at hand.

Too many young people somehow have the feeling that there is something undesirable about "big business"; and in particular, there is something shady about making a profit. I very much fear that some teachers are guilty of encouraging such attitudes. A teacher can do great harm this way. To be blunt about it, such an attitude cannot reflect much intelligence. Why? A teacher lives on a salary. (I ought to know; I lived on mine for half a century.) Where does that salary come from? Taxes. Where do taxes come from? They come from *successful* profit-making enterprises in farming, business, and industry; and from taxes paid by people who work for these enterprises. Taxes furthermore support the government, for law enforcement, defense, public health, public works, and so on. When an enterprise fails, it stops paying taxes. The making of a profit is of absolutely vital concern to the continuation of our economy.

If, in that economy, a firm's continued success depends in part on retaining the right to patents taken out by its employees, then it must retain that right. And that's the way it is.

FIFTEEN

Conclusion

Were you born too late? What if most of the discoveries and inventions have already been made? We had better discuss that. And then, there's some more to say about education as related to creativity, and about innovation.

EDUCATION AND CREATIVITY

Present trends in the colleges, in the teaching of the physical sciences and engineering, may be operating so that a large number of our most creative people will never get to realize their full creative potentialities.

Science and engineering have greatly expanded in content, complexity, and the corresponding need for mathematics training. Our faculties and administrators, driven by that pressure, strive to keep up with the torrent. In the engineering area, more and more of engineering reality is squeezed out, as more time is found for teaching the science back of engineering. In the physical sciences, more theory and more reliance on mathematics is the order of the day. As many are pointing out, the curricula, the texts, and the teaching are more and more directed to preparing B.S. graduates to go on for an advanced degree.

This trend completely ignores the fact that any number of highly creative science-minded and engineering-minded young people have scant interest in mathematics; many have such low aptitude that they never get into college; or if they do, they soon leave.

Why are college faculties and administrators showing so little concern about this, a problem of great national importance? I have very good reason to think that one explanation is this: Few of them know anything about creativity and the creative process—even though some are innately creative and achieve high productivity.

Another reason may stem from the fact that today, our teaching staffs are made up almost entirely of men with the Ph.D. A large majority have won that degree by virtue of their high capacity to be scholars—able to handle advanced theory and mathematics. They naturally tend to breed more of their own kind, which they do; and to add more of their own kind to the teaching staff, which they do. It is entirely natural for them to assume that the way to advance science and technology is to keep on running the same kind of educational enterprise. We must now add in the fact that very high scholarship gives no guarantee whatever that it is accompanied by high creativity, or even an interest in creativity. It may or may not be.

These trends will not be quickly reversed, if ever. Certainly, we must continue to turn out graduates in quantity, who can take advantage of advanced training, and make the contributions that can only come by building on a large base of science and mathematics. But what provision is there for these others, about whom at least some concern should be expressed? Let us remind ourselves of two of these others.

The man who did more to change man's thinking for the next century than anyone else was a dropout, and almost a double dropout. His wealthy father, a physician, tried to make a doctor out of him. It didn't work. Next, he planned to make a clergyman out of the young failure. That didn't work either. Then the young man, at age twenty-three, left England for a voyage on *The Beagle,* as a naturalist. He returned five years later, world-famous. In 1859, he published *Origin of Species.* His name was Charles Darwin. He never really used mathematics above plain arithmetic; and as nearly as I can make out, he was a fumbler at that.

The man who gave us much of our broad foundations in electricity and magnetism was the world's greatest creative genius at experimentation. Mathematically, he mastered only plain arithmetic, and there is no reason to think he could have gone any higher. Michael Faraday, of course.

In the typical college or university of today, there is no place for a Faraday or a Darwin. How long can we afford to let this tragic waste of talent continue?

Meantime, you in high school, with creative talents but without the grades to get into college: What are you going to do about it? One possibility is to become a technician. Another is to go on in a technical institute. In either case, alertness, wide reading, and whatever self-training is needed may enable you, in a few years, to find the right niche, and make some of the limitless contributions yet to be made that do not require the training of a Ph.D.

DISCOVERIES AHEAD

Is there really much of science left to be discovered, or is the big show nearly over? You are, of course, fully aware of how the physical sciences, several times, have seemed to be all settled, when Bang!—everything broke loose and a new start had to be made. That is history, and it gives no proof that it will happen again. But it warns us that it might.

Right now, we are stretching our imaginations, facilities, and creativity in two fantastically opposite directions. While we are using great instrumental resources to probe the nucleus of the atom (where everyone is in quite a dither about what goes on), we are using other great resources to probe space and the universe, and making one discovery after another. It is as certain as can be that these two sets of phenomena will keep everyone in these areas busy and happy at unraveling the mysteries—with plenty left over for your grandchildren to work on. Many other areas offer like promise.

Consider the biological sciences. They too have had their periods of calm shattered, with new starts having to be made. Not too long ago, teaching what was known about the cell was not difficult. There it was, and there were its parts, revealed by the microscope. Then came the electron microscope, and other ways of revealing many things that had been hidden. Genetics took on new life, with new mysteries to be unraveled by research on the genes. Biochemistry has made tremendous strides. And where is the cell today? The more we learn about it, the more "impossible" it seems to be. A fantastic thing, perhaps crammed with more puzzles than will be solved in a thousand years, if ever.

Are there discoveries yet to be made? Draw your own conclusions.

INVENTIONS AHEAD

Were you born too late to be an inventor? After all, patents have been issued by the millions. How could there be much left to invent? A fair question. It deserves some hard-and-fast discussion.

An invention makes a hitherto unknown combination out of known parts or items or elements, whatever these may be. Let us consider inventions combining just four elements, such as bimetal. It requires two different metals (that's two), plus a process for welding them together (that makes three), plus a heat treatment to give reliability under working conditions (that's four). Two materials, two processes. Now think of the number of materials and processes available to you today, compared to what were available to Benjamin Franklin. In materials, think of the metallic alloys we have: thousands, or more. Think of our ceramics and glasses. Add in plastics, once nonexistent except for a few natural ones, and we seem to be getting only well started on plastics. You can add other classes of materials Franklin never knew.

Then, processes. We go to near absolute zero to do strange things. By nuclear reactions, we hope to go up to twenty million degrees Centigrade. By new processes we grow pure whisker crystals having fantastic strength. We are doing great things with thin films, so that a giant computer can be squeezed down to a hatful of integrated circuits. You take it from there. You read about these things as they come along, and you can add plenty of examples to my meager list representing our expanding technology.

And now, back to our sample type of invention requiring only four elements. If our expanding technology, in a decade, doubles the number of elements available (materials, processes, etc.), would that merely *double* the number of possible new combinations? Take a simple example and some paper, and see how you come out. This isn't any little arithmetic progression. Its nature is that of a *geometric* progression.

When you think of it that way, you might even get a sort of desperate feeling: How in the world will there ever be enough creative people to tap all of the useful combinations even now available to us—let alone all those new ones to be born every day?

Were you born too late? I leave the conclusion to you.

INVENTING BACKWARD

We are so used to the constant effort to improve our products that when we find an inventor taking a long step backward, we might wonder what's wrong with him. Consider the washing of clothes. It used to be done by hand power, with tub and washboard. Then came the hand-operated washing machine. Next, a machine with motor drive. Next, constant improvement of the washer, in one way or another. Why, then, try to invent a good hand-operated washing device? Who in the world would buy it? Even so, there is a Boston inventor, Richard R. Walton. And there is Robert W. Young, vice president in charge of worldwide marketing, of the Colgate-Palmolive Company. Young persuaded Walton to get busy and see what he could do.

Walton is a strictly cut-and-try man, who never works from drawings. He is an experimenter, with a "feel" for things. After months of work in his basement, Walton developed a washer to handle four pounds of clothes in five gallons of water. The handle of a lever is moved up and down. There is a vertical cylinder. The piston, going down, pushes sudsy water out through holes near the bottom. Going up, it sucks the water back in. After trying many variations of sizes of parts and so on, Walton came out with an excellent washer.

There was still one trouble: the upstroke required a lifting force, and that was tiring. He solved that by a lucky accident, when he happened to use a piston made of lightweight plastic: its buoyancy did the lifting for the operator (and what a simple answer that was!).

Walton spent a week "in the field": he went to a poor Mexican community. The women flocked to see the demonstrations. They were enthusiastic! Do you begin to see some sense to "inventing backward"? There are several hundred million women in the world who still have to get on hands and knees by a stream to do the washing. The hope is to get these machines made in Mexico for three dollars or less, and relieve humanity of one great burden!

INNOVATION

Creativity brings out something new. *Innovation* is the matter of getting the new thing adopted and into use. The discoverer or inventor, it is true, can be called an innovator, if you wish. For certainly, his creation has the potentiality for innovation. But whether it will be taken up and adopted, or not, can depend on various factors. If it does succeed, innovation has taken place. Often, and perhaps nearly always, innovation takes place at the hands of others. The inventor of a good gadget may have no means of getting it to the market. But if he licenses a firm to make it, and the public buys it, there is innovation.

As a kid on the farm six decades ago, I used to help make the yellow soap used for the family washing. Today, the housewife takes her sack of clothes to a laundromat. Think of all the innovations that mark the way from washboard to the automatic washer! And now comes another that will eliminate the washing: paper clothing. Wear it, throw it away!

Creativity leads to innovation and change in every human

activity that can be changed. It is not confined to discoveries in science, to understand more about stars and atoms; nor to engineering, to give us more and better gadgets; nor to agriculture, to give us more peaches per tree and bushels of wheat per acre. Long ago, the awkward business of barter and exchange of actual goods was simplified by an innovation: hard money. Later, pieces of paper representing hard money made the exchange operations easier still. The complex operations of banking and finance all came about through innovations gradually invented and adopted.

It is my hope that some young creatives have stayed with me this far, even though having little interest in physics, internal combustion engines, or ways to get to the other side of the moon. If so, you too have joined the Creativity Club. By means of the creative process, you may become those who will help solve our pressing human problems. We *must* have your innovations if we are to survive.

Returning to the science-minded, and your goal—be it to become an astronomer, nuclear physicist, inventor, or—you name it. Go to it, and do your very best. We need you. But in doing so, you are not relieved of all responsibility to your fellow man. Give some thought to lending spare-time talents and your full support to your fellow creative workers who will innovate for the direct benefit of society.

APPENDIX

Two Problems in Invention (Chapter Two)

The Ball-Dropping Problem. I can only give you my personal convictions. First, it is impossible: no static device can ever do the job. Second, no one will ever prove that it is, or is not possible.

The Aluminum Sheet. After rolling the sheet as thin as can be and it is twice as thick as desired, simply feed *two* of those sheets together through the rolls.

America's Greatest Inventors

John C. Patterson's book, having the above title, covers the lives and contributions of our eighteen greatest inventors, as selected in 1940 by a distinguished committee of scientists and industrialists. This was in connection with the United States Patent Law Sesquicentennial Celebration. The committee was headed by Dr. Charles F. Kettering.

Patterson says, "To be a great inventor, one should perhaps choose a clergyman for a father. Six of the eighteen were clergymen's sons. That proportion is slightly high, because the airplane is credited to two inventors, the Wright brothers, sons of a United Brethren bishop, but even so the clergy has produced far more than its share of great inventors. The other four are Morse, Bell, Tesla, and De Forest. Not one of these eighteen came from a family of wealth. Without exception they made far more money than their fathers ever did. Four of the eighteen were born in Europe. Eight were college graduates, several of them with Ph.D's. Edison and the Wright brothers were among those who never even went through high school. Almost all showed signs of distinction well before they were 30."

The Eighteen

Eli Whitney	Cotton gin
Robert Fulton	Steamboat
Cyrus Hall McCormick	Reaper
Samuel F. B. Morse	Telegraph
Charles Goodyear	Vulcanizing of rubber
Elias Howe	Sewing machine
Christopher Latham Sholes	Typewriter
George Westinghouse, Jr.	Air brake; many others
Alexander Graham Bell	Telephone
Thomas Alva Edison	The greatest: 1093 patents
Nikola Tesla	Induction motor; generators, transformers
Charles Morton Hall	Hall process, making aluminum
Ottmar Mergenthaler	Linotype
Wright brothers	Airplane
Lee De Forest	Audion tube
Leo Hendrik Baekeland	Father of plastics. Bakelite
William M. Burton	Cracking of petroleum to make gasoline

Patents and the Patent System

For many centuries, a monopolistic right called a patent was granted to individuals or enterprises by royalty, or the state. These included the permission to explore, and to hold title to lands discovered. A king might pay off a debt by giving a creditor the exclusive right to engage in a certain kind of business, such as making and vending salt. Note this: The man who got that right had not invented anything. This meant that something that had been in the public domain and belonged to everybody, was taken from everybody and given to him. It was this kind of abuse that eventually led to reform.

By the sixteenth century, patents were being issued to citizens in several nations, giving the exclusive right to make and sell things they had invented. In our country in colonial days, each colony had its own, though very inadequate patent practices. Then the Constitution handed control of patents to Congress, and the patent law of 1790 was passed. It was better, but also inadequate. It did not require a *novelty search*—thus two or more patents on the same invention might be issued. Many cases of conflicting claims arose, breeding patent litigation and chaos. The later patent law of 1836, and subsequent laws, require the patent office to make a search to determine novelty. This greatly reduces the chance of issuing a patent on something already patented; or on an invention that is not new, whether patented or not.

I am much indebted to Robert A. Choate for carefully checking this section on patents and the patent system, and for making valued clarifications. He lectures on patent law in our Law School at the University of Michigan, and is a member of the Detroit patent law firm of Barnes, Kisselle, Raisch & Choate.

The Invention and the Patent

The invention, and the patent on the invention, are two entirely different things. The invention is a *concept*. The patent is a *contract*.

The whole philosophy of the patent system is to wipe out secrecy, and get the public informed of the invention and how to use it. If secrecy prevailed, the inventor would take grave risks. Secrets "will out"; and a device being made in secrecy, or a process being carried out, would too easily have its secret betrayed. Very few inventors would care to take that risk, and there would be little innovation. A firm might spend huge sums at perfecting a process or product of great benefit to humanity—only to have its secrets stolen by just one dishonest employee.

In quite the opposite way, the U.S. patent system says to the inventor, Come out in the open; tell us what you have; make your claims about it; we will make a search and do our best to find if it is new; if it is new, and if it really amounts to invention—then we will issue a patent to you; and we will sell a copy of your patent to anyone, for fifty cents. We thereby give you the right, for seventeen years, to prevent unauthorized (that is, unlicensed) persons from making, using, or selling your invention.

Again: The invention is a concept. The patent protecting it is a contract.

Official Gazette

The *Official Gazette of the U. S. Patent Office* is issued weekly, and sells for fifty dollars per year. Each issue lists patents granted in a week. The patents are very briefly described. Usually, one key drawing is included, with the description. Patented inventions are thus revealed, and anyone can then send for full copies of patents.

What Can Be Patented

A patent can be issued on a new mechanism, process, or composition of matter if the contribution has novelty (that is, if it is really new); if it promises to be useful (at least remotely so); and if it has the element of "invention" in it.

The present statute says that the idea must be unobvious to persons having ordinary skill in the particular field in which the invention is made. We will illustrate this. Let us assume that the ordinary lawnmower does not exist, and now, John Doe invents one. He has not made one and tried it out, but he wants to. Suppose he brings his drawings to me (assume that I run a general-purpose machine shop). I agree to build the device. After he leaves, my men gather around to look at his drawings, and have a big laugh. Poor John Doe has woefully poor judgment about strength of materials: His drawings show a solid steel shaft two inches in diameter!

I build his mower with a far smaller, lighter, tubular shaft. The lawnmower works. He gets his patent. Then I have second thoughts. Didn't I *improve* John Doe's machine? I surely did, when I cut that ridiculously heavy shaft down to size. I apply for an *improvement* patent. It is refused. Or, if mistakenly issued, it would promptly be thrown out, in a suit. Why? The courts have repeatedly ruled on this kind of thing: I have merely done for John Doe what "one skilled in the art" was expected to do. This is a simple, clear-cut example. But as you might guess, this is a border-line area in which honest differences of opinion can sometimes arise, and a judge may be hard put to make the right decision.

Another thing about an invention: No matter how ingenious, if it would operate against the public welfare, it cannot be patented. Example: a gambling device; or one that can only be used to deceive or defraud.

Another thing: Only a real person can apply for a patent. And the "inventor" may become "inventors" when more than one person actually contributes to the invention; it is then called a *joint* invention.

A firm, company, or corporation cannot invent, and cannot apply for a patent. Real persons do that. After a patent comes to an employee, he typically assigns the patent to the firm.

The Right to Make, Use, and Sell

At times, the law can be so wordy that a layman gets lost among the verbal profusions. At other times it can be notoriously brief. This time, it is brief. When an uninformed amateur inventor gets that beautiful, seal-decorated patent, and reads about a ". . . right to make, use, and sell . . . ," he thinks he really has it made. How soon can he start in business, and all that? The answer may be, never.

Some of our widely known guarantees are the rights to life, liberty, and the pursuit of happiness. But we soon learn that there are spoken and unspoken limits to these things. I am at liberty, and I have a right to use the sidewalk. Some fellow blocks my path. He has no right to do that. Using my liberty, I open up my pocket knife and stimulate him to get out of my way by inserting the blade into one of his soft spots for half an inch. He removes himself. But then, I go to a cell, where all of my liberties are curtailed. In short, other people have rights, too. Yes, he overstepped the bounds when he blocked me; but I had no right to resort to such severe measures. I could have walked around him.

Back to the patent. What it really is saying is that the inventor has the right to prevent others (if not licensed) from making, using, or selling his invention. It does not *need* to say that it cannot give him the right to violate the rights of someone else. We are all expected to know that. For example, my patented idea may turn out to be an infringement of an earlier patent on a broader invention. Or let's say that it is for an improvement on the automobile. I don't build cars, and never will. So I go to those who do. They have their own patent departments, and they all have copies of my patent, on file, before I get there. They decide, one by one, not to use my improvement. What can I do about it? Nothing. Maybe it is hard for me to see why, at an added cost of only a dollar, they are so dumb. But they can honestly point to all of the hundreds of improvement inventions having an equal claim; and which, if all were stacked onto the car, would price it out of the market, and also make it look like a Christmas tree on a spree. They have their problems too, you know.

Who Takes Out Patents?

J. Herbert Holloman writes on "The U. S. Patent System" in *Scientific American*, June 1967. He states that 5 per cent of all patents go to inventors in government and nonprofit institutions; 70 per cent go to inventors in private industry, half of these going to employees in *small* industries. The remainder, 25 per cent, go to independent inventors. Thus, the prospects for the independent inventor are still very bright. He says, "In this century alone individual inventors and small companies have made such outstanding inventive contributions as the vacuum tube, xerography, DDT, metallic titanium, the zipper, frequency-modulated radio, the self-winding wrist watch, the helicopter, power steering, air conditioning and the Polaroid camera."

He cites a study of seven major inventions dealing with petroleum refining, and says that all seven came from independent inventors. Another study was made of 149 inventions in the aluminum industry; of the seven regarded as most important, only one came from a major producer.

I would remind you that it is facts such as these that are making the large firms try harder, by enlarging their R & D (research and development) departments, and by being very interested in finding how to make team research more productive. The large firm does have this advantage: It can tool up for production while waiting for the patent to be issued; whereas the small firm or the individual can seldom afford to do this, and will be delayed in getting to the market. Also, the large firm is usually in a much better position to make an adequate search of prior patents and the literature and to know that the patent sought will likely be issued than is the small firm or the independent.

About one patent in a thousand is issued to a woman.

Publication Limit: One Year

Every inventor should be keenly aware of the fact that if he publishes his invention before applying for his patent, he may do so, but he must apply for the patent within one year from date of publication. What legally constitutes publication is a question having its own complications. Space here does not permit going into that.

In fact, any release to the public, such as to sell some of the invented items has, under certain conditions, the same limit.

Basic Patents and Improvement Patents

When young Hall used cryolite and aluminum oxide, added direct current and the heat made by the current, he became the first to produce aluminum electrolytically, and at a low price. His patent was *basic*. As technology developed, many *improvement* patents were taken out on improvements made.

Inherently, basic patents are rare. If a basic patent covers a commercially successful invention, it can be extremely valuable.

Volume of Patents in the United States

According to Holloman, the backlog of pending patent applications now comes to over 200,000. In fiscal 1966, action was concluded on 91,059 applications, from which 66,-243 patents were issued. That was a record. But a new record was set by *new* applications to the number of 93,022—thereby putting the Patent Office still further behind.

Patent Law Reform

It now takes an average of two and a half years after application for the Patent Office to issue the patent; and it often takes longer. There is every reason to wish that this time lag could be shortened.

Another problem of staggering proportions comes from trying to get patent protection abroad. A patent issued in one country covers the rights only in that country. If an American inventor wants to be covered, say, in West Germany, he has to file for a West German patent on the same invention. This is called multiple filing.

Practically everyone is agreed on the need for reform; much attention has been given to the problems, and a major report, with recommendations, is now under sharp discussion. Really effective reform will take time, and a lot of doing. One thing is certain: It won't please everyone.

Patent Costs

The filing fee now averages eighty-five dollars. The final fee, paid at time of issue, is around an average of one hundred forty dollars. So much for the government end of it.

In addition, there is the cost of preparing the application. It is rare indeed that the inventor can prepare it himself. Unless he has learned the Patent Office rules and knows *exactly* how to follow them, he cannot do it at all. But even more important, and aside from the matter of form, he runs extremely serious risks in trying to write his own claims. He may get a very weak patent issued for an invention that deserves support from strong claims. In short, he must have the expert services of a good patent attorney. I understand that this part of the cost seldom runs below five hundred dollars.

Records

In the United States, the law says that the patent goes to the first inventor, when two or more applications covering the same invention are filed. What this really means—and has to mean—is that it goes to the man who has *proof* that he was first: proof for the Patent Office; and possibly, proof that will later stand up in court if there is a suit. Thus, the simple intent of the law can be turned into some beautiful hassles.

The prime way to avoid trouble and disappointment is to *keep records*. Not just any old records. Satisfactory records, made in certain accepted ways, of the conception of the invention and the actual testing of it. Space does not permit going further into this extremely important matter. Suffice it to be said that if you work for an invention-conscious firm, you will speedily learn all about such records, and you will have no choice whatever: *Those records will be kept.* You may be required to make daily entries in a *bound* journal. You may be required, daily, to sign or initial the journal, and any other sketches, drawings, or notes produced in connection with the thing under development. A firm is not pleased when it loses a million-dollar suit because some employee failed in one of these respects.

Patterson (see *America's Greatest Inventors*) tells what happened when Alexander Graham Bell invented the telephone. "Soon, Bell had a patent on the telephone, and scores of inventors and pseudo-inventors claimed that they had preceded him in making the simple discovery. In all Bell was involved in more than five hundred patent suits, but again and again the courts ruled that he was the inventor, and only the patent system protected his invention from being pirated. Probably no patent was ever the center of more legal dispute. Once a diagram on the back of a sheet of paper, inadvertently sent to a school for the deaf, giving advice on teaching methods, was resurrected as evidence to prove that Bell had preceded another inventor in developing a vital detail."

You see, a court has to act on proof, and not just the claims someone may make. Where would Bell have been without adequate proof?

Closing Remarks

You have read a bare outline of some of the high spots concerning patents, patent law, and the patent law situation. This is just enough to get you into deep trouble, if you assume you are now well set to go ahead on your own. There is much more to it. A number of books, and a good many papers are available. They can be freely consulted. This is a highly complex subject, with its rules, exceptions, court decisions, and so on. The independent inventor especially, needs to acquire a very considerable background before he can safely proceed on his own.

The employed inventor has the advantage here. His firm is anxious to help him be productive and to conserve his time. It will pay all of the costs, and its patent department will stand by to give every assistance and take care of the technicalities.

Finally, for some readers, two suggestions. First, why not think of heading into patent law, by becoming a patent attorney? You would constantly be dealing with creative minds in highly varied situations; and your ingenuity would be called on to the utmost, either in serving your clients to secure good patents, or in court to represent them. A usual way is to take an engineering degree; then, instead of going on for a Ph.D., you take law. I have helped more than one of my engineering students to make this decision, and they have never regretted it.

I have great respect for good patent attorneys. One of my

treasured experiences was to be taken on as expert witness by a patent attorney firm, to help the firm prepare to defend a patent infringement suit.

We worked on that preparation, off and on, for about a year. A large sum of money was spent—a good deal of it going to extensive tests that involved using engineers and technicians, much equipment, and the making of motion pictures to present in court. The tests (all of which I had to witness) were thorough. The total preparation was so thorough, in fact, that the attorneys won "for our side" by a settlement out of court. My one regret was that in not going to trial, I did not have the fun of watching the battle in court, and taking part in it.

The second suggestion: Take up being an expert witness as a profession. No, not soon. You need poise, background, maturity. You would first—after getting some experience—set up as a consulting engineer in some broad line of work. You would be available to help an individual or a firm to perfect an invention, or to carry out tests to support a case in a patent suit. One such expert recently consulted me: He had a case coming up in which he was out of his element, and it concerned phenomena within one of my lines of interest. He spends practically all of his time preparing for patent suits, and being an expert witness in the ensuing court cases.

Robert Choate tells me there is a great need for qualified people to enter both of the areas suggested.

RECOMMENDED READING

BEVERIDGE, W. I. B. *The Art of Scientific Investigation*. New York: Random House, 1957. By a noted British scientist, it is the pre-eminent book of its kind.

BOYS, SIR CHARLES VERNON. *Soap Bubbles and the Forces which Mould Them*. Garden City, N.Y.: Doubleday & Company, Inc., 1959. Science Study Series S3. Reprint of a famous book of 1890, by a remarkable character. He was unbelievably skillful in making apparatus. The accuracy with which Boys measured the gravitational constant was not improved on for fifty years.

BROWN, SANBORN C. *Count Rumford—Physicist Extraordinary*. Garden City, N.Y.: Doubleday & Company, Inc., 1962. Science Study Series S28. A fascinating account of the man who combined the qualities of great scoundrel, great organizer, and great originator.

CAMERON, FRANK. *Cottrell—Samaritan of Science*. Garden City, N.Y.: Doubleday & Company, Inc., 1952. Sooner or later, every scientist and engineer should read this book about a great pioneer.

CRAIG, RICHARD A. *The Edge of Space—Exploring the Upper Atmosphere*. Garden City, N.Y.: Doubleday & Company, Inc., 1968. Science Study Series S55. After reading of the great and varied research yet to be done on our atmosphere, anyone who thinks there is little left to discover and invent will change his mind.

DIBNER, BERN. *Ten Founding Fathers of the Electrical Science*. Norwalk, Conn.: Burndy Library, Inc. 1954. Brief, authoritative accounts of the contributions of ten of the greats, from William Gilbert to James Clerk Maxwell.

DUBOS, RENE. *Pasteur and Modern Science*. Garden City, N.Y.: Doubleday & Company, Inc., 1960. Science Study Series S15. An eminent biologist's exciting story of the man whose spectacular discoveries and prophetic vision continue to acquire increased significance as modern science develops.

FROMAN, ROBERT. *Wanted: Amateur Scientists*. New York: David McKay Company, 1963. Any youngster will find this book inspiring.

GARDNER, JOHN W. *Self-Renewal—The Individual and the Innovative Society*. New York: Harper & Row, 1963. One of the most important books of our time. Gardner was recently in the Cabinet as Secretary of Health, Education, and Welfare.

JAFFE, BERNARD. *Michelson and the Speed of Light*. Garden City, N.Y.: Doubleday & Company, Inc., 1960. Science Study Series S13. The stimulating story of America's first Nobel Prize winner.

JOSEPHSON, MATTHEW. *Edison*. New York: McGraw-Hill Book Company, 1959. A fine biography of America's greatest inventor.

MACDONALD, D. K. C. *Faraday, Maxwell, and Kelvin*. Garden City, N.Y.: Doubleday & Company, Inc., 1964. Science Study Series S33. A charming account of the lives and contributions of three of our greatest.

MUSSELMAN, M. M. *Wheels in His Head*. New York: McGraw-Hill (Whittlesey House), 1945. Musselman's hilarious story of the life of his father—inventor of the coaster brake and the airplane landing tire—is just too good to miss.

NEWHALL, BEAUMONT. *Latent Image—The Discovery of Photography*. Garden City, N.Y.: Doubleday & Company, Inc., 1967. Science Study Series S54. The struggles of Daguerre, Talbot, and others in discovering photography *before* science was advanced enough to be of much help.

OSBORN, ALEX. *Your Creative Power*. New York: Charles Scribner's Sons, 1948. Many accounts of creative men and instances.

PATTERSON, JOHN C. *America's Greatest Inventors*. New York: Thomas Y. Crowell Company, 1943. The careers and contributions of the eighteen inventors selected in 1940 as our greatest.

PUPIN, MICHAEL. *From Immigrant to Inventor*. New York: Charles Scribner's Sons, 1930. Autobiography. Perfectly fascinating!

WILLIAMS, JOHN K. *The Wisdom of Your Subconscious Mind*. Englewood Cliffs, N.J.: Prentice-Hall, 1964. Highly readable.

WILSON, MITCHELL. *American Science and Invention*. New York: Bonanza Books, 1960. The fabulous story of how

American dreamers and inspired tinkers converted a wilderness into the wonder of the world. A great book by a thoroughly competent writer.

FOR ADULTS

BERLE, A. K. AND DE CAMP, L. S. *Inventions, Patents, and their Management.* Princeton, N.J.: D. Van Nostrand Company, 1959. Authoritative and comprehensive.

COHEN, I. BERNARD. *Franklin and Newton.* Cambridge, Mass.: Harvard University Press, 1966. A monumental book, thoroughly researched. The stature of these two giants will be greatly increased for all who read it.

NATIONAL ACADEMY OF SCIENCES. *Applied Science and Technological Progress.* Washington, D.C. Superintendent of Documents, U. S. Government Printing Office, June 1967. Excellent discussions and case histories of the very broad subject.

SELYE, HANS. *From Dream to Discovery.* New York: McGraw-Hill Book Company, 1964. This book "on being a scientist" is by the famed originator of the concept of physiological *stress.* A masterful book by a master. Selye's pungent comments alone make it a welcome contribution. There are many other values.

TAYLOR, C. W. AND BARRON, FRANK. *Scientific Creativity: Its Recognition and Development.* New York: John Wiley & Sons, 1966. The outcome of three conferences held at the University of Utah. By twenty-nine contributors.

THOMSON, SIR GEORGE. *The Inspiration of Science.* New York: Oxford University Press, 1961. George Thomson, son of J. J. Thomson, shared, with Davisson, a Nobel Prize in Physics. A fine book about science, scientists, and how some discoveries were made.

THOMSON, J. J. *Recollections and Reflections.* London, England: G. Bell and Sons, 1936. Autobiographical and historical; an absorbing book by the discoverer of the electron.

WILLIAMS, L. PEARCE. *Michael Faraday.* New York: Basic Books, 1965. A splendid biography of our greatest experimenter.